Maths Progress
Support Book

Series editors: Dr Naomi Norman and Katherine Pate
Authors: Jack Barraclough, Sharon Bolger, Catherine Murphy and Amy O'Brien

3

Pearson

Published by Pearson Education Limited, 80 Strand, London, WC2R 0RL.

www.pearsonschoolsandfecolleges.co.uk

Text © Pearson Education Limited 2019
Project managed and edited by Just Content Ltd
Typeset by PDQ Digital Media Solutions Ltd
Original illustrations © Pearson Education Limited 2019
Cover illustration by Robert Samuel Hanson

The rights of Nick Asker, Jack Barraclough, Sharon Bolger, Gwenllian Burns, Greg Byrd, Lynn Byrd, Andrew Edmondson, Bobbie Johns, Catherine Murphy, Naomi Norman, Amy O'Brien, Mary Pardoe, Katherine Pate, Harry Smith and Angela Wheeler to be identified as authors of this work have been asserted by them in accordance with the Copyright, Designs and Patents Act 1988.

First published 2019

22 21 20 19
10 9 8 7 6 5 4 3 2 1

British Library Cataloguing in Publication Data
A catalogue record for this book is available from the British Library.

ISBN 978 1 292 27994 7

Printed in Italy by LEGO S.p.A

Note from the publisher
Pearson has robust editorial processes, including answer and fact checks, to ensure the accuracy of the content in this publication, and every effort is made to ensure this publication is free of errors. We are, however, only human, and occasionally errors do occur. Pearson is not liable for any misunderstandings that arise as a result of errors in this publication, but it is our priority to ensure that the content is accurate. If you spot an error, please do contact us at resourcescorrections@pearson.com so we can make sure it is corrected.

Contents

Maths Progress Second Edition

Confidence at the heart

Maths Progress Second Edition is built around a unique pedagogy that has been created by leading mathematics educational researchers and Key Stage 3 teachers in the UK. The result is an innovative structure, based around 10 key principles designed to nurture confidence and raise achievement.

Pedagogy – our 10 key principles

- Fluency
- Problem-solving
- Reflection
- Mathematical Reasoning
- Progression
- Linking
- Multiplicative Reasoning
- Modelling
- Concrete - Pictorial - Abstract (CPA)
- Relevance

This edition of Maths Progress has been updated based on feedback from thousands of teachers and students.

The Core Curriculum

Textbooks with tried-and-tested differentation

Core Textbooks *For your whole cohort*

Based on a single, well-paced curriculum with built-in differentiation, fluency, problem-solving and reasoning so you can use them with your whole class. They follow the unique unit structure that's been shown to boost confidence and support every student's progress.

Support Books
Strengthening skills and knowledge

Provide extra scaffolding and support on key concepts for each lesson in the Core Textbook, giving students the mathematical foundations they need to progress with confidence.

Depth Books
Extending skills and knowledge

Deepen students' understanding of key concepts, and build problem-solving skills for each lesson in the Core Textbook so students can explore key concepts to their fullest.

Welcome to Maths Progress Second Edition Support Books!

Master
Learn fundamental knowledge and skills over a series of lessons.

Key point   Explain key concepts and definitions where students need them.

Hints
Guide students to help build problem-solving strategies throughout the course.

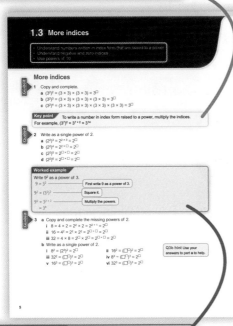

Worked example
Provides guidance around examples of key concepts with images, bar models, and other pictorial representations where needed.

Reflect   Metacognitive questions that ask students to examine their thinking and understanding.

Guided questions
Provide extra scaffolding or partially completed answers to help students work through questions step by step.

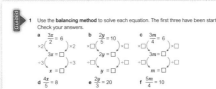

The Support Book is designed to give students additional scaffolding and support on key concepts contained in each Core Textbook lesson. It gives students the mathematical foundations they need to progress with confidence.
Depth books are available for students who would benefit from additional problem-solving content and further stretch.

Progress with confidence!

This innovative Key Stage 3 Mathematics course builds on the first edition KS3 Maths Progress (2014) course, drawing on input from thousands of teachers and students, and a 2-year study into the effectiveness of the course. All of this has come together with the latest cutting-edge approaches to shape Maths Progress Second Edition.

Take a look at the other parts of the series

*Active*Learn Service

The *Active*Learn service enhances the course by bringing together your planning, teaching and assessment tools, as well as giving students access to additional resources to support their learning. Use the interactive Scheme of Work, linked to all the teacher and student resources, to create a personalised learning experience both in and outside the classroom.

What's in ActiveLearn for Maths Progress?

- ✓ **Front-of-class student books** with links to PowerPoints, videos, animations and homework activities

- ✓ **96 new KS3 assessments and online markbooks,** including end-of-unit, end-of-term and end-of-year tests

- ✓ **Over 500 editable and printable homework worksheets** linked to each lesson and differentiated for Support, Core and Depth

- ✓ **Online, auto-marked homework activities**

- ✓ **Interactive Scheme of Work** makes re-ordering the course easy by bringing everything together into one curriculum for all students with links to Core, Support and Depth resources, and teacher guidance

- ✓ **Student access to videos, homework and online textbooks**

ActiveLearn Progress & Assess

The Progress & Assess service is part of the full ActiveLearn service, or can be bought as a separate subscription. It includes assessments that have been designed to ensure all students have the opportunity to show what they have learned through:

- a 2-tier assessment model
- approximately 60% common questions from Core in each tier
- separate calculator and non-calculator sections
- online markbooks for tracking and reporting
- mapped to indicative 9–1 grades

New *Assessment Builder*

Create your own classroom assessments from the bank of Maths Progress assessment questions by selecting questions on the skills and topics you have covered. Map the results of your custom assessments to indicative 9–1 grades using the custom online markbooks. *Assessment Builder* is available to purchase as an add-on to the *Active*Learn Service or Progress & Assess subscriptions.

Purposeful Practice Books

Over 3,750 questions using minimal variation that:

- ✓ build in small steps to consolidate knowledge and boost confidence
- ✓ focus on strengthening skills and strategies, such as problem-solving
- ✓ help every student put their learning into practice in different ways
- ✓ give students a strong preparation for progressing to GCSE study

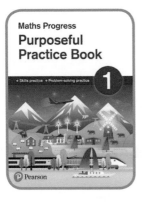

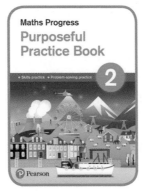

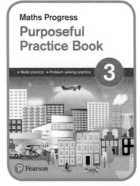

1 Indices and standard form

1.1 Indices

- Calculate combinations of indices, fractions and brackets
- Use index laws to simplify expressions

Priority of operations including negative numbers and powers

Guided

1 Copy and complete.

a $(-2)^2 = -2 \times -2 = \square$

b $(-2)^3 = -2 \times -2 \times -2 = \square$

c $(-2)^4 = -2 \times -2 \times -2 \times -2 = \square$

d $(-2)^5 = \square \times \square \times \square \times \square \times \square = \square$

Q1a hint Remember: negative × negative = positive

Q1b hint Remember: negative × negative × negative = positive × negative = negative

2 Decide whether each statement is true or false.

a $(-1)^2 = 1^2$ **b** $(-2)^2 = 2^2$ **c** $(-3)^2 = 3^2$ **d** $(-4)^2 = 4^2$

e $(-1)^3 = 1^3$ **f** $(-1)^4 = 1^4$ **g** $(-1)^5 = 1^5$ **h** $(-1)^6 = 1^6$

Guided

3 Copy and complete.

a $(-2)^2 + 1 = (-2 \times -2) + 1 = \square + 1 = \square$

b $1 + (-2)^2 = 1 + (-2 \times -2) = \square + \square = \square$

c $(-2)^2 - 1 = (\square \times \square) - \square = \square - \square = \square$

d $1 - (-2)^2 = 1 - (\square \times \square) = \square - \square = \square$

e $5^2 - (-2)^2 = (5 \times 5) - (-2 \times -2) = 25 - \square = \square$

f $1^2 + (-3)^2 = (1 \times \square) + (-3 \times \square) = \square + \square = \square$

g $(-10)^2 - (-9)^2 = (\square \times \square) - (\square \times \square) = \square - \square = \square$

Q3a hint Follow the priority of operations: do indices before addition and subtraction.

4 Reasoning Tom says, '1 + (−2)² gives the same answer as 1 − 2².' Is he correct?

Q4 hint Work out the indices first.

Using the index laws to simplify expressions

Guided

1 Copy and complete.

a $2^3 = 2 \times \square \times \square$ **b** $2^4 = 2 \times 2 \times \square \times \square$

c $2^3 \times 2^4 = (2 \times \square \times \square) \times (2 \times 2 \times \square \times \square) = 2^\square$

1

2 Copy and complete to write as a single power of 3.

a $3^2 \times 3^2 = (3 \times 3) \times (3 \times 3) = 3^\square$

b $3^2 \times 3^3 = (3 \times 3) \times (3 \times 3 \times 3) = 3^\square$

c $3^2 \times 3^4 = (3 \times 3) \times (3 \times \square \times \square \times \square) = 3^\square$

d $3^2 \times 3^5 = (3 \times 3) \times (3 \times \square \times \square \times \square \times 3) = 3^\square$

e $3^2 \times 3^6 = (\square \times \square) \times (\square \times \square \times \square \times \square \times \square \times 3) = 3^\square$

f What do you notice about the power in the answers to parts **a–e**?

Key point When multiplying powers of the same number you can add the indices (powers).

Worked example

Write $12^3 \times 12^5$ as a single power of 12.

$12^3 \times 12^5 = 12^{3+5}$ —————— Add the powers together.

$\qquad\qquad = 12^8$

3 Copy and complete to write as a single power of 5.

a $5^3 \times 5^7 = 5^{3+\square} = 5^\square$

b $5^4 \times 5^{11} = 5^{\square+\square} = 5^\square$

c $5 \times 5^3 = 5^{1+3} = 5^\square$

d $5^7 \times 5 = 5^{7+\square} = 5^\square$

Worked example

Write $7^8 \div 7^3$ as a single power of 7.

$7^8 \div 7^3 = \dfrac{7^8}{7^3}$ —————— Write the division as a fraction.

$\qquad = \dfrac{7 \times 7 \times 7 \times 7 \times 7 \times 7 \times 7 \times 7}{7 \times 7 \times 7}$

$\qquad = \dfrac{{}^1\!\!\!\diagup\!\!\!7 \times {}^1\!\!\!\diagup\!\!\!7 \times {}^1\!\!\!\diagup\!\!\!7 \times 7 \times 7 \times 7 \times 7 \times 7}{{}^1\!\!\!\diagup\!\!\!7 \times {}^1\!\!\!\diagup\!\!\!7 \times {}^1\!\!\!\diagup\!\!\!7}$ —————— Simplify the fraction by dividing the numerator and denominator by $7 \times 7 \times 7$.

$\qquad = 7 \times 7 \times 7 \times 7 \times 7$

$\qquad = 7^5$

4 Copy and complete to write as a single power of 3.

a $3^5 \div 3^3 = \dfrac{3^5}{3^3} = \dfrac{3 \times 3 \times 3 \times 3 \times 3}{3 \times 3 \times 3} = \square \times \square = \square$

b $3^4 \div 3^2 = \dfrac{3^\square}{3^2} = \dfrac{\square \times \square \times \square \times \square}{3 \times 3} = \square \times \square = \square$

c $3^5 \div 3^3 = \dfrac{3^\square}{3^2} = \dfrac{\square \times \square \times \square \times \square \times \square}{3 \times 3 \times 3} = \square \times \square = \square$

Reflect In this lesson you have learned about indices. Write three things you need to know when calculating using indices. Compare your list with a partner's.

1.2 Calculations and estimates

- Calculate with powers and roots
- Estimate answers to calculations

Estimating powers and roots

> **Key point** To find the cube root of a number $\sqrt[3]{\ }$ find the number that is multiplied by itself three times to give that number.

Guided

1 Copy and complete. The first one has been done for you.

a $1^3 = 1 \times 1 \times 1 = 1$ therefore $\sqrt[3]{1} = 1$

b $2^3 = 2 \times 2 \times 2 = 8$ therefore $\sqrt[3]{8} = \square$

c $3^3 = \square \times \square \times \square = \square$ therefore $\sqrt[3]{27} = \square$

d $(-1)^3 = -1 \times -1 \times -1 = \square$ therefore $\sqrt[3]{-1} = \square$

e $(-2)^3 = -2 \times -2 \times -2 = \square$ therefore $\sqrt[3]{-8} = \square$

f $(-3)^3 = \square \times \square \times \square = \square$ therefore $\sqrt[3]{\square} = -3$

2 Keenan is working out an estimate for $\sqrt{95}$.

He says, 'I know that $\sqrt{81}$ is 9 and $\sqrt{100}$ is 10. Using a number line, I can see that $\sqrt{95}$ is closer to $\sqrt{100}$ than $\sqrt{81}$. Therefore $\sqrt{95}$ is approximately 10.'

Use Keenan's method to work out whether 9 or 10 is the best estimate for

a $\sqrt{83}$ b $\sqrt{89}$ c $\sqrt{92}$ d $\sqrt{99}$

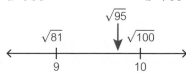

Guided

3 Copy and complete to find an estimate for each square root.

a $\sqrt{16} = 4$ and $\sqrt{25} = \square$ therefore $\sqrt{18}$ is approximately $\square$

b $\sqrt{4} = \square$ and $\sqrt{9} = \square$ therefore $\sqrt{8}$ is approximately $\square$

c $\sqrt{36} = \square$ and $\sqrt{49} = \square$ therefore $\sqrt{40}$ is approximately $\square$

d $\sqrt{121} = \square$ and $\sqrt{144} = \square$ therefore $\sqrt{125}$ is approximately $\square$

> **Q3a hint**
> Draw a number line like the one in **Q2**.

Guided

4 Saira is estimating $\sqrt[3]{21}$.

She writes a list of the cube numbers: 1, 8, 27, 64, 125, ...

She sees that 21 is closest to 27 so she says, '$\sqrt[3]{21}$ is approximately 3'.

a Use Saira's method to estimate

i $\sqrt[3]{7}$ ii $\sqrt[3]{30}$ iii $\sqrt[3]{2}$

iv $\sqrt[3]{110}$ v $\sqrt[3]{99}$ vi $\sqrt[3]{12}$

b Copy and complete.

$-1^3 = -1$ $-2^3 = -8$ $-3^3 = \square$ $-4^3 = \square$ $-5^3 = \square$

c Estimate

i $\sqrt[3]{-7}$ **ii** $\sqrt[3]{-30}$ **iii** $\sqrt[3]{-2}$

iv $\sqrt[3]{-110}$ **v** $\sqrt[3]{-99}$ **vi** $\sqrt[3]{-12}$

> **Q4c hint** Your answers to part **a** should help.

Estimating calculations

Worked example

Estimate $4.91 + 3.25^2 \times 1.91$

$4.91 + 3.25^2 \times 1.91 \approx 5 + 3^2 \times 2$ —— Round each number to the nearest whole number.

$\approx 5 + 9 \times 2$ —— Follow the priority of operations – do indices first.

$\approx 5 + 18$ —— Do multiplication or division before addition or subtraction.

≈ 23

Guided

1 Copy and complete to estimate the answers.

> **Q1 hint** $\approx$ means 'is approximately equal to'.

a $3.42 \times (8.61 - 3.9) \approx 3 \times (9 - \square)$

$\approx 3 \times \square$

$\approx \square$

b $4.25^2 - 5.62 \approx 4^2 - \square$

$\approx \square - \square$

$\approx \square$

c $(9.35 - 2.1)^2 \approx (\square - \square)^2$

$\approx \square^2$

$\approx \square$

d $\sqrt{102} \times 5.43 \approx \sqrt{100} \times \square$

$\approx \square \times \square$

$\approx \square$

e $\sqrt[3]{9} + 8.7 \approx \sqrt[3]{8} + \square$

$\approx \square + \square$

$\approx \square$

f $2.8 \times \sqrt[3]{-28} \approx \square \times \sqrt[3]{-27}$

$\approx \square \times \square$

$\approx \square$

2 Reasoning Alice is buying three DVDs, which cost £5.99 each, and two books, which cost £8.45 each.

a Estimate the total cost.

b Will your estimate be more than or less than the actual cost? Explain why you think this.

Reflect   Write a list of the maths skills you used in this lesson.

Discuss with a partner the question you found most difficult in this lesson.

1.3 More indices

- Understand numbers written in index form that are raised to a power
- Understand negative and zero indices
- Use powers of 10

More indices

Guided

1 Copy and complete.
   a $(3^2)^2 = (3 \times 3) \times (3 \times 3) = 3^\square$
   b $(3^2)^3 = (3 \times 3) \times (3 \times 3) \times (3 \times 3) = 3^\square$
   c $(3^2)^4 = (3 \times 3) \times (3 \times 3) \times (3 \times 3) \times (3 \times 3) = 3^\square$

> **Key point** To write a number in index form raised to a power, multiply the indices.
> For example, $(3^7)^2 = 3^{7 \times 2} = 3^{14}$

Guided

2 Write as a single power of 2.
   a $(2^2)^3 = 2^{2 \times 3} = 2^\square$
   b $(2^2)^4 = 2^{2 \times \square} = 2^\square$
   c $(2^2)^5 = 2^{\square \times \square} = 2^\square$
   d $(2^2)^6 = 2^{\square \times \square} = 2^\square$

> **Worked example**
>
> Write 9^2 as a power of 3.
>
> $9 = 3^2$ ———————— First write 9 as a power of 3.
>
> $9^2 = (3^2)^2$ ———————— Square it.
>
> $9^2 = 3^{2 \times 2}$ ———————— Multiply the powers.
>
> $\quad = 3^4$

Guided

3 a Copy and complete the missing powers of 2.
   i $8 = 4 \times 2 = 2^2 \times 2 = 2^{2 + 1} = 2^\square$
   ii $16 = 4^2 = 2^2 \times 2^2 = 2^{\square + \square} = 2^\square$
   iii $32 = 4 \times 8 = 2^\square \times 2^\square = 2^{\square + \square} = 2^\square$

   b Write as a single power of 2.
   i $8^2 = (2^3)^2 = 2^\square$
   ii $16^2 = (\square^\square)^2 = 2^\square$
   iii $32^2 = (\square^\square)^2 = 2^\square$
   iv $8^3 = (\square^\square)^3 = 2^\square$
   v $16^3 = (\square^\square)^3 = 2^\square$
   vi $32^3 = (\square^\square)^3 = 2^\square$

> **Q3b hint** Use your answers to part **a** to help.

4 **a** Copy and complete the missing powers of 3.

   i $9 = 3^{\square}$ **ii** $27 = 3^{\square}$ **iii** $81 = 3^{\square}$

 b Write as a single power of 3.

   i $9^3 = (\square^{\square})^3 = 3^{\square}$ **ii** $27^3 = (\square^{\square})^3 = 3^{\square}$ **iii** $81^3 = (\square^{\square})^3 = 3^{\square}$

Positive and negative powers of 10

1 **Problem-solving**

 a Copy and complete this place value table.

	Millions	Hundred thousands	Ten thousands	Thousands	Hundreds	Tens	Ones	.	Tenths $\left(\frac{1}{10}\right)$	Hundredths $\left(\frac{1}{100}\right)$	Thousandths $\left(\frac{1}{1000}\right)$
10^6	1	0	0	0	0	0	0	.	0	0	0
10^5		1	0	0	0	0	0	.	0	0	0
10^4								.			
10^3								.			
10^2								.			
10^1								.			
10^0								.			
10^{-1}								.			
10^{-2}								.			
10^{-3}								.			

 b Copy and complete. Choose one of the options in the circle.

   A positive power of 10 is _____ 1.

   A negative power of 10 is _____ 1.

   10^0 is _____ 1.

> smaller than
> larger than
> equal to

 c Copy and complete to write each negative power of 10 as a fraction. The first one has been done for you.

> **Q1c hint** Use the place value table to help you.

   i $10^1 = 10$ and $10^{-1} = \frac{1}{10^1} = \frac{1}{10}$

   ii $10^2 = \square$ and $10^{-2} = \frac{1}{10^2} = \frac{1}{\square}$

   iii $10^3 = \square$ and $10^{-3} = \frac{1}{10^3} = \frac{1}{\square}$

   iv $10^4 = \square$ and $10^{-4} = \frac{1}{10^4} = \frac{1}{\square}$

 d Write each answer to part **c** as a decimal.

> **Reflect** What did you notice about negative powers of 10? What effect would multiplying by a negative power of 10 have?

1.4 Standard form

- Write large and small numbers using standard form

Multiplying by positive and negative powers of 10

1 **a** Copy and complete the pattern.

$2 \times 10 = \square$

$2 \times 10^2 = 2 \times 10 \times 10 = \square$

$2 \times 10^3 = 2 \times 10 \times 10 \times 10 = \square$

$2 \times 10^4 = 2 \times \square \times \square \times \square \times \square = \square$

$2 \times 10^5 = 2 \times \square \times \square \times \square \times \square \times \square = \square$

b Copy and complete the pattern.

$30 = 3 \times 10 = \square$

$300 = 3 \times 10 \times 10 = 3 \times 10^2$

$3000 = 3 \times 10 \times 10 \times 10 = 3 \times 10^{\square}$

$30\,000 = 3 \times \square \times \square \times \square \times \square = 3 \times 10^{\square}$

$300\,000 = 3 \times \square \times \square \times \square \times \square \times \square = 3 \times 10^{\square}$

Worked example

Work out 3×10^{-3}.

$10^{-3} = \dfrac{1}{1000} = 0.001$ ⎯⎯⎯⎯⎯⎯⎯ [Write 10^{-3} as a decimal.]

$3 \times 10^{-3} = 3 \times 0.001 = 0.003$

---

2 Work out

a 4×10^{-1} **b** 4×10^{-2} **c** 4×10^{-3} **d** 5×10^{-1} **e** 5×10^{-2} **f** 5×10^{-3}

3 **Reasoning**

a Miguel says that dividing by 10^2 and multiplying by 10^{-2} give the same answer. Is he correct?

b Miguel also says that dividing by 10^3 and multiplying by 10^{-3} give the same answer. Is he correct?

Standard form

> **Key point** Very large and very small numbers are often written in **standard form**.
> A number is written in standard form when a number between 1 and 10 is multiplied by a power of 10. For example, $3\,000\,000$ can be written in standard form as 3×10^6.

1 Write each number in standard form.

a $2000 = 2 \times 1000 = 2 \times 10^{\square}$ **b** $60\,000 = 6 \times 10\,000 = 6 \times 10^{\square}$

c $900 = 9 \times 100 = 9 \times 10^{\square}$ **d** $80\,000 = 8 \times \square = 8 \times 10^{\square}$

2 **Reasoning** Jacqui and Al are writing the number 12 000 in standard form.

Jacqui writes:

$12\,000 = 12 \times 1000$

$= 12 \times 10^3$

Al writes:

$12\,000 = 1.2 \times 10\,000$

$= 1.2 \times 10^4$

What mistake has Jacqui made?

3 **Problem-solving** Which of the three options shows the original number written in standard form?

Q3 hint The number being multiplied by a power of 10 **must** be between 1 and 10.

a 340 000 **A** 34×10^4 **B** 3.4×10^5 **C** 3.4×10^6

b 1230 **A** 1.23×10^3 **B** 123×10 **C** 1.23×10^4

c 150 **A** 1.50×10 **B** 1.5×10^2 **C** 15×10

d 14 000 000 **A** 14×10^6 **B** 1.4×10^6 **C** 1.4×10^7

4 Copy and complete.

$0.2 = 2 \div 10 = 2 \times 10^{-1}$

$0.02 = 2 \div 100 = 2 \times 10^{-\square}$

$0.002 = 2 \div 1000 = 2 \times 10^{-\square}$

$0.0002 = 2 \div 10\,000 = 2 \times 10^{-\square}$

$0.000\,02 = 2 \div 100\,000 = 2 \times 10^{-\square}$

Worked example

Write 0.000 07 in standard form.

$0.000\,07 = 7 \div 100\,000$ —— Work out the power of 10 that 7 has been divided by.

$= 7 \div 10^5$ —— $\div 10^5$ is the same as $\times 10^{-5}$

$= 7 \times 10^{-5}$

---

5 **a** Copy and complete.

  i $0.0003 = 3 \div 10\,000 = 3 \div 10^4 = 3 \times 10^{\square}$

  ii $0.004 = 4 \div \square = 4 \div 10^3 = 4 \times 10^{\square}$

  iii $0.05 = 5 \div \square = 5 \div 10^{\square} = 5 \times 10^{\square}$

  iv $0.000\,06 = 6 \div \square = 6 \div 10^{\square} = 6 \times 10^{\square}$

b Write 0.000 000 000 3 in standard form: $3 \times 10^{\square}$

Q5a hint Dividing by 10^4 is the same as multiplying by 10^{-4}.

6 **Problem-solving** Which of the three options shows the original number written in standard form?

a 0.000053 **A** 53×10^{-6} **B** 5.3×10^{-5} **C** $5.3 \div 10^5$

b 0.15 **A** $15 \div 10^2$ **B** 1.5×10^{-1} **C** 15×10^{-2}

c 0.0105 **A** 1.5×10^{-2} **B** 1.05×10^2 **C** 1.05×10^{-2}

d 0.000 11 **A** $11 \div 10^{-5}$ **B** 1.1×10^{-4} **C** $1.1 \div 10^4$

Reflect Do you think it is easier to read very large or very small numbers in standard form? Explain.

Guided

Guided

2 Expressions and formulae

2.1 Solving equations

- Write and solve equations with fractions
- Write and solve equations with the unknown on both sides

Solving equations involving fractions

Worked example

Use the **balancing method** to solve $\frac{2x}{3} = 4$.

$$\frac{2x}{3} = 4$$

$\times 3 \left(\right) \times 3$

$$2x = 12$$

$\div 2 \left(\right) \div 2$

$$x = 6$$

Do the same thing to both sides of the equation.

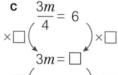

$x \rightarrow \boxed{\times 2} \rightarrow \boxed{\div 3} \rightarrow 4$

$\Box \leftarrow \boxed{\div 2} \leftarrow \boxed{\times 3} \leftarrow 4$

Check: $\frac{2 \times 6}{3} = \frac{12}{3} = 4$ ✓

Check your answer is correct by substituting your answer into the equation.

Guided

1   Use the **balancing method** to solve each equation. The first three have been started for you. Check your answers.

a $\frac{3x}{2} = 6$

$\times 2 \left(\right) \times 2$

$3x = \Box$

$\div 3 \left(\right) \div 3$

$x = \Box$

b $\frac{2y}{5} = 10$

$\times \Box \left(\right) \times \Box$

$2y = \Box$

$\div \Box \left(\right) \div \Box$

$y = \Box$

c $\frac{3m}{4} = 6$

$\times \Box \left(\right) \times \Box$

$3m = \Box$

$\div \Box \left(\right) \div \Box$

$m = \Box$

d $\frac{4x}{5} = 8$ e $\frac{2y}{3} = 20$ f $\frac{5m}{4} = 10$

Solving equations with fraction solutions

Guided

1   Write these calculations as fractions. The first one has been done for you.

a $1 \div 2 = \frac{1}{2}$ b $2 \div 5 = \frac{\Box}{5}$ c $2 \div 3 = \frac{\Box}{\Box}$ d $5 \div 2 = \frac{\Box}{\Box}$

2   Solve these equations.

a $2x = 3$ b $4x = 5$ c $8x = 9$ d $5x = 3$

3 Use the balancing method to solve these equations. The first three have been started for you.
Check your answers.

a $2a + 3 = 13$

$-3 \Big(\Big) -3$

$2a = \square$

$\div\square \Big(\Big) \div\square$

$a = \square$

b $2x + 5 = 12$

$-5 \Big(\Big) -5$

$2x = \square$

$\div\square \Big(\Big) \div\square$

$x = \square$

c $3m - 1 = 9$

$+1 \Big(\Big) +1$

$3m = \square$

$\div\square \Big(\Big) \div\square$

$m = \square$

d $4x + 2 = 15$

e $5p - 1 = 17$

f $2x - 3 = 14$

Solving two-step equations involving fractions

Worked example

Use the balancing method to solve $\dfrac{x}{2} + 4 = 6$.

$\dfrac{x}{2} + 4 = 6$

$-4 \Big(\Big) -4$ Subtract 4 first to get the x-term on its own.

$\dfrac{x}{2} = 2$

$\times 2 \Big(\Big) \times 2$

$x = 4$

$$x \rightarrow \boxed{\div 2} \rightarrow \boxed{+4} \rightarrow 6$$
$$\square \leftarrow \boxed{\times 2} \leftarrow \boxed{-4} \leftarrow 6$$

Check: $\dfrac{4}{2} + 4 = 2 + 4 = 6$ ✓

1 Solve these equations. They have been started for you.

a $\dfrac{a}{2} + 4 = 10$

$-4 \Big(\Big) -4$

$\dfrac{a}{2} = \square$

$\times 2 \Big(\Big) \times 2$

$a = \square$

b $\dfrac{x}{3} + 1 = 8$

$-1 \Big(\Big) -1$

$\dfrac{x}{3} = \square$

$\times\square \Big(\Big) \times\square$

$x = \square$

c $\dfrac{p}{4} - 3 = 13$

$+3 \Big(\Big) +3$

$\dfrac{p}{4} = \square$

$\times\square \Big(\Big) \times\square$

$p = \square$

Worked example

Use the balancing method to solve $\dfrac{x + 4}{2} = 6$.

$\dfrac{x + 4}{2} = 6$

$\times 2 \Big(\Big) \times 2$ Multiply by 2 first to remove the fraction.

$x + 4 = 12$

$-4 \Big(\Big) -4$

$x = 8$

$$x \rightarrow \boxed{+4} \rightarrow \boxed{\div 2} \rightarrow 6$$
$$\square \leftarrow \boxed{-4} \leftarrow \boxed{\times 2} \leftarrow 6$$

Check: $\dfrac{8 + 4}{2} = \dfrac{12}{2} = 6$ ✓

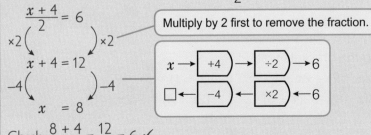

2 Solve these equations. The first three have been started for you.

a $\dfrac{x+5}{2} = 6$

$\times 2 \left(\quad\right) \times 2$

$x + 5 = \square$

$-5 \left(\quad\right) -5$

$x = \square$

b $\dfrac{x+4}{3} = 2$

$\times 3 \left(\quad\right) \times 3$

$x + 4 = \square$

$-4 \left(\quad\right) -\square$

$x = \square$

c $\dfrac{a-2}{5} = 2$

$\times 5 \left(\quad\right) \times 5$

$a - 2 = \square$

$+\square \left(\quad\right) +\square$

$a = \square$

d $\dfrac{x+6}{2} = 5$

e $\dfrac{p-1}{3} = 4$

f $\dfrac{m-3}{4} = 2$

Solving equations with unknowns on both sides

1 Use the balancing method to solve this equation.

$2x + 3 = x + 10$

$-x \left(\quad\right) -x$

$\square + 3 = 10$

$-3 \left(\quad\right) -3$

$x = \square$

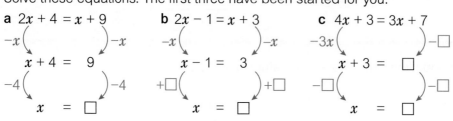

$2x + 3 - x = x + 10 - x$

$\square + 3 - 3 = 10 - 3$

$x = \square$

2 Solve these equations. The first three have been started for you.

a $2x + 4 = x + 9$

$-x \left(\quad\right) -x$

$x + 4 = 9$

$-4 \left(\quad\right) -4$

$x = \square$

b $2x - 1 = x + 3$

$-x \left(\quad\right) -x$

$x - 1 = 3$

$+\square \left(\quad\right) +\square$

$x = \square$

c $4x + 3 = 3x + 7$

$-3x \left(\quad\right) -\square$

$x + 3 = \square$

$-\square \left(\quad\right) -\square$

$x = \square$

d $3x - 2 = 2x + 5$

e $4x + 2 = 3x + 4$

f $3x - 5 = 2x + 3$

3 Solve these equations. The first one has been started for you.

a $4x = 2x + 8$

$-2x \left(\quad\right) -2x$

$2x = 8$

$\div 2 \left(\quad\right) \div 2$

$x = \square$

b $3x = x + 10$

c $5x = 2x + 9$

4 Solve these equations. Expand the brackets first.

a $2(x + 3) = x + 10$

b $3(x - 2) = 2x + 5$

c $4(x - 1) = 3x + 2$

d $3(x - 2) = x + 4$

e $3(x - 1) = 2(x + 5)$

f $3(2x + 4) = 2(2x + 10)$

Reflect

What is the same and what is different about $\dfrac{x + 1}{3} = 5$ and $\dfrac{x}{3} + 1 = 5$? How does this affect the way you solve each one?

2.2 Substituting into expressions

- Use the priority of operations when substituting into algebraic expressions
- Substitute values into expressions involving powers and roots

Guided

Substituting values into expressions involving powers and roots

1 Work out

  a $3^2 = 3 \times 3 = \square$

  b 6^2

  c 5^2

  d $2^3 = 2 \times 2 \times 2 = \square$

  e 1^3

  f 4^3

  g $\sqrt{49}$

  h $\sqrt{25}$

  i $\sqrt{9}$

2 Work out the value of each expression.

  a x^2 when $x = 4$

  b y^2 when $y = 7$

  c a^2 when $a = 0.5$

  d m^3 when $m = 3$

  e p^3 when $p = 2$

> **Q2a hint** When $x = 4$, $x^2 = \square \times \square = \square$

Guided

3 Work out the value of each expression when $a = 3$.

  a $a^2 + 4 = \square \times \square + 4 = \square$

  b $a^2 - 4$

  c $a^2 + 3$

  d $a^2 - 3$

  e $a^2 + a$

  f $a^2 - a$

Guided

4 Work out the value of each expression when $b = 2$.

  a $b^3 + 2 = \square \times \square \times \square + 2 = \square$

  b $b^3 - 2$

  c $b^3 + 5$

  d $b^3 - 5$

  e $b^3 + b$

  f $b^3 - b$

5 Work out the value of each expression.

   a $2c^2$ when $c = 4$ **b** $3d^2$ when $d = 1$

   c $2k^2 + 1$ when $k = 2$ **d** $2m^2 + 3$ when $m = 2$

   e $3p^2 + 4$ when $p = 2$ **f** $2a^3$ when $a = 3$

   g $3p^3$ when $p = 2$ **h** $2n^3 + 1$ when $n = 1$

   i $2n^3 - 2$ when $n = 2$

6 Work out the value of each expression when $a = 4$ and $b = 2$.
   The first two have been started for you.

   a $a^2 + b = \square \times \square + 2 = \square$

   b $a^2 + b^2 = \square \times \square + 2 \times 2 = \square$

   c $2a^2 + b$ **d** $a^2 - b^2$

   e $2a^2b$ **f** $2ab^2$

> **Q6e–f hint** The power relates to the number or letter immediately to the left. $2a^2b$ means $2 \times a^2 \times b$ or $2 \times a \times a \times b$

Substituting values into expressions involving brackets

> **Key point**   The **priority of operations** is
>
> **B**rackets → **I**ndices (powers) → **D**ivision and **M**ultiplication → **A**ddition and **S**ubtraction

1 Copy and complete for $x = 2$ and $y = 3$.

   a $(2y)^2 = (2 \times 3)^2 = 6 \times 6 = \square$

   b $(3x)^2 = (3 \times \square)^2 = \square \times \square = \square$

   c $(4x)^2 = (\square \times \square)^2 = \square \times \square = \square$

   d $(x + 1)^2 = (\square + 1)^2 = \square \times \square = \square$

   e $(3 + y)^2 = (\square + \square)^2 = \square \times \square = \square$

   f $(x + y)^2 = (\square + \square)^2 = \square \times \square = \square$

   g $2(x + y) = 2 \times (\square + \square) = 2 \times \square = \square$

   h $3(x + y) = 3 \times (\square + \square) = \square$

   i $5(x - y) = \square \times (\square - \square) = \square$

   j $(xy)^2 = (\square \times \square)^2 = \square \times \square = \square$

> **Q1j hint** Work out the value of xy first. xy means $x \times y$.

2 Copy and complete for $p = 3$ and $q = 4$.

   a $(p + 2q)^2 = (3 + 2 \times 4)^2 = \square^2 = \square$

   b $(p + 3q)^2 = (3 + 3 \times \square)^2 = \square^2 = \square$

   c $(2p + q)^2 = (\square \times \square + 4)^2 = \square^2 = \square$

   d $(2p - q)^2 = (\square \times \square - 4)^2 = \square^2 = \square$

   e $(p + q)^2 + 1 = (\square + \square)^2 + 1 = \square^2 + 1 = \square$

   f $(p + q)^2 + 3 = (\square + \square)^2 + \square = \square^2 + \square = \square$

   g $(p + q)^2 - 2 = (\square + \square)^2 - \square = \square^2 - \square = \square$

3 Work out the value of each expression when $a = 2$ and $b = 12$. The first two have been started for you.

a $\dfrac{a}{2} = \dfrac{\square}{2} = \square$

b $\dfrac{b}{3} = \dfrac{\square}{3} = \square$

c $\dfrac{a + b}{2}$

d $\dfrac{2a + b}{4}$

e $\dfrac{ab}{4}$

f $\dfrac{a + b}{a}$

4 Work out the value of each expression.

a $\sqrt{x}$ when $x = 4$ b $\sqrt{y}$ when $y = 100$

5 Work out the value of each expression when $x = 9$ and $y = 7$.

a $\sqrt{x}$ b $\sqrt{4x}$ c $\sqrt{x + y}$

6 Work out the value of each expression when $m = 8$ and $n = 27$.

a $\sqrt[3]{m}$ b $\sqrt[3]{n}$

7 Work out the value of each expression when $a = 1$, $b = 4$ and $c = 3$.

a $a + (b \times c) = 1 + (4 \times 3)$
$$= 1 + \square$$
$$= \square$$

> **Q7a hint** Remember the priority of operations. Do brackets before addition.

b $b + (c - a)$

c $a^2 \times (b - c)$

d $b^2(c - a)$

e $2b(c^2 + a)$

f $2b(c^2 + 2a)$

g $b(c + a) + 5$

h $b(c + a) + b$

8 Work out the value of each expression when $a = -2$, $b = 3$ and $c = 5$.

a $4a$ b ab c $a + c$

d $b(a + c)$ e $b(a + c^2)$ f $b(a^2 + c)$

g $b(a^2 + c) + b$

> **Q8f hint**
> $-2^2 = (-2)^2 = -2 \times -2 = \square$

> **Reflect** What is the same and what is different when you substitute $a = 4$ in the expressions $2a^2$ and $(2a)^2$?

Writing and using formulae

Guided

1 Write an expression for the output of each function machine.
The first one has been done for you.

a $a \rightarrow \boxed{\times 3} \rightarrow a \times 3$ or $3a$

b $b \rightarrow \boxed{\times 5} \rightarrow$ _____

c $p \rightarrow \boxed{+4} \rightarrow$ _____

d $s \rightarrow \boxed{-10} \rightarrow$ _____

Guided

2 Copy and complete each function machine.
Write an expression with the unknown number n.
The first one has been done for you.

a Double n add 4.

$n \rightarrow \boxed{\times 2} \rightarrow \boxed{+4} \rightarrow n \times 2 + 4$ or $2n + 4$

b Subtract 4 from n then multiply by 3.

$n \rightarrow \boxed{.....} \rightarrow \boxed{.....} \rightarrow$ _____

> **Q2b hint** When multiplying an expression involving addition or subtraction, remember to use brackets: $\Box(n - \Box)$

c Add 3 to n then double.

$n \rightarrow \boxed{.....} \rightarrow \boxed{.....} \rightarrow$ _____

d Multiply n by 2 then subtract 4.

$n \rightarrow \boxed{.....} \rightarrow \boxed{.....} \rightarrow$ _____

Guided

3 Michael buys some cakes. The cost of each cake is 90p.
Copy and complete this function machine and write the formula for the cost, C, in pence, of buying x cakes.

$x \rightarrow \boxed{\times 90} \rightarrow 90\Box \qquad C = 90\Box$

4 Joe buys some glue sticks.

The cost of each glue stick is 20 pence.

Copy and complete this formula for the total cost, C, in pence, of buying g glue sticks.

$C = \square \times g$ or $C = \square g$

5 Mary buys some rulers.

The cost of each ruler is 50 pence.

Write a formula for the cost, C, in pence, of r rulers.

Q5 hint $C =$ ....

6 The cost of a theatre ticket is £10.

a Copy and complete the formula for the cost, C, in £, of t tickets.

$C = \square \times \square = \square$

b Work out the cost of 6 tickets.

Worked example

Paula rents a car.

The cost, C, of renting a car is £20 per day plus a £25 deposit.

a Use this function machine to write a formula for the cost, in £, of renting the car for n days.

$$n \rightarrow \boxed{\times 20} \rightarrow \boxed{+25} \rightarrow 20n + 25$$

$C = 20n + 25$

b How much will it cost to rent the car for 4 days?

$C = 20 \times 4 + 25 = £105$

It will cost £105.

---

7 The cost of hiring a trailer is £30 per day plus a £20 deposit.

a Copy and complete this formula for the cost, C, in £, of hiring the trailer for d days.

$C = 30 \times \square + 20$ or $C = 30\square + 20$

b How much will it cost to hire the trailer for 2 days?

Graphs and formulae

The graph shows the cost of hiring a canoe.

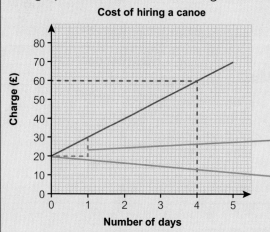

Cost of hiring a canoe

The cost is £10 per hour.

This is a fixed charge just for hiring the canoe. It is the same no matter how long the canoe is hired for.

a There is a fixed charge for hiring a canoe. How much is it?

£20

b How much will it cost to hire a canoe for 4 days?

20 + 10 × 4 = £60 — Total cost = fixed charge + cost for 4 days

1 The graph shows the amount a gardener charges her customers.

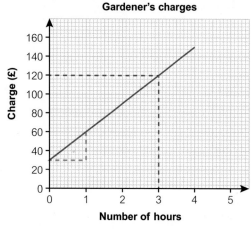

Gardener's charges

a How much is the gardener's call-out fee?

b How much does the gardener charge for 1 hour of work?

c How much does the gardener charge for 3 hours' work?

Q1b hint How much does the price increase in the first hour?

d Copy and complete this formula for the charge, C, in £, for h hours worked.

$$C = \square h + \square$$

Reflect It costs £10 per hour to rent a boat with a deposit of £20.

Simon says the formula for the cost of renting a boat is $C = 20h + 10$.

What mistake has Simon made? Write the correct formula.

2.4 Using and rearranging formulae

- Substitute into formulae and then solve equations to find unknown values
- Change the subject of a formula

Substituting values, then solving an equation

Worked example

Use the formula $M = P + Q$ to work out the value of

a M when $P = 4$ and $Q = 5$

$M = P + Q$

$\quad = 4 + 5$

$\quad = 9$

b P when $M = 6$ and $Q = 2$

$M = P + Q$

$6 = P + 2$

$-2 \big(\quad\big) -2$

$4 = P$

$P = 4$

> Write your answer with the subject on the left-hand side, $P = ...$

c Q when $M = 10$ and $P = 3$

$M = P + Q$

$10 = 3 + Q$

$-3 \big(\quad\big) -3$

$7 = Q$

$Q = 7$

1 Use the formula $T = R + S$ to work out the value of

   a T when $R = 10$ and $S = 3$ **b** S when $T = 4$ and $R = 3$

   c R when $S = 6$ and $T = 9$

2 Use the formula $L = P - Q$ to work out the value of

   a L when $P = 6$ and $Q = 1$ **b** P when $L = 4$ and $Q = 3$

3 Use the formula $d = st$ to work out the value of

   a d when $s = 3$ and $t = 5$ **b** s when $d = 20$ and $t = 4$

   c t when $d = 30$ and $s = 10$

4 Use the formula $A = \dfrac{F}{H}$ to work out the value of

   a A when $F = 15$ and $H = 5$ **b** F when $A = 6$ and $H = 4$

5 The formula for the mean, M, of two values a and b is $M = \frac{1}{2}(a + b)$.
Copy and complete to work out the mean of a and b.

a $a = 6$ and $b = 2$ $\qquad M = \frac{1}{2}(6 + 2) = \frac{1}{2} \times \square = \square$

b $a = 3$ and $b = 10$ $\qquad M = \frac{1}{2}(\square + \square) = \frac{1}{2} \times \square = \square$

Rearranging formulae

1 Rearrange each equation to show how you would work out the missing value.
The first one has been done for you.

a $m + 4 = 10$

$-4 \big(\qquad \big) -4$

$m = 10 - 4$

b $p - 2 = 5$

$+\square \big(\qquad \big) +\square$

$p = \square + \square$

c $2a = 10$

$\div\square \big(\qquad \big) \div\square$

$a = \dfrac{\square}{\square}$

d $\dfrac{s}{5} = 3$

$\times\square \big(\qquad \big) \times\square$

$s = \square$

Worked example

Rearrange $M + 3 = N$ to make M the subject.

$M + 3 = N$

$-3 \big(\qquad \big) -3$ —— Use the inverse operation of +3 to get M on its own.

$M = N - 3$ —— Making M the subject means writing the formula as $M = ...$

$M \rightarrow \boxed{+3} \rightarrow N$

$M \leftarrow \boxed{-3} \leftarrow N$

---

2 Copy and complete to make P the subject of each formula.

a $P + 2 = S$
$P = S - \square$

b $P - 3 = S$
$P = S + \square$

c $P + 4 = 2S$
$P = 2S - \square$

d $P - 6 = 3S$
$P = \square + \square$

3 Copy and complete to make M the subject of each formula.

a $5M = N$
$M = \dfrac{N}{\square}$

b $3M = 2N$
$M = \dfrac{2N}{\square}$

c $\dfrac{M}{2} = N$
$M = \square N$

d $\dfrac{M}{4} = 2N$
$M = \square N$

> **Q3 hint** Remember to do the inverse operation.

Rearrange $S = 3T$ to make T the subject.

$S = 3T$

$\div 3 \Big(\quad \Big) \div 3$

$\dfrac{S}{3} = T$

$T = \dfrac{S}{3}$

$T \rightarrow \boxed{\times 3} \rightarrow S$

$T \leftarrow \boxed{\div 3} \leftarrow S$

4   Make T the subject of each formula.

    a $P = 4T$ **b** $X = 6T$

    c $\dfrac{T}{6} = Y$ **d** $\dfrac{T}{a} = Z$

    e $bT = Q$ **f** $R = cT$

5   Make P the subject of each formula.

    a $M = P + 5$ **b** $M = P - 4$

    c $M = 6P$ **d** $M = \dfrac{P}{5}$

6   Make S the subject of each formula.

    a $T = S + R$ **b** $T = S - R$

    c $T = SR$ **d** $T = \dfrac{S}{R}$

Guided

7   Make x the subject of each formula.
   The first one has been started for you.

    a $y = 2x + c$

       $y - \square = 2x$

          $2x = y - \square$

             $x = \dfrac{y - \square}{\square}$

    b $y = 2x - c$

    c $3y = 2x + 4c$

    d $3y = 2x - 5c$

Reflect   Mark rearranged the formula $T = 3P + S$ to make P the subject.

He said the answer was $P = \dfrac{T}{3} - S$.

What has Mark done wrong? Write the correct answer.

2.5 Index laws and brackets

- Use the rules for indices for multiplying and dividing
- Simplify expressions involving brackets
- Factorise an expression by taking out an algebraic common factor

Rules of indices

Key point   Any number to the power of zero is 1.

Guided

1 Copy and complete.

   a $2^3 \times 2^4 = (2 \times 2 \times 2) \times (2 \times 2 \times 2 \times 2) = 2^{\square}$

   b $3^2 \times 3^3 = (\square \times \square) \times (\square \times \square \times \square) = 3^{\square}$

   c 5×5^4

   d $7^4 \times 7^2$

   e $a^7 \times a^3$

   f $y^5 \times y$

   g Reasoning What do you notice about the answers to parts **a–f**?

> **Q1c hint** 5 is the same as 5^1

Key point   The base number stays the same when you calculate with powers.

Guided

2 Simplify

   a $2a^2 \times 3a^3 = 2 \times a^2 \times 3 \times a^3 = 2 \times 3 \times \square^2 \times \square^3$

                                   $= 6\square^{\square}$

   b $4a^3 \times 2a^4 = 4 \times 2 \times a^3 \times a^4$

                     $= \square a^{\square}$

   c $3b^2 \times 4b^5$

   d $2x^2 \times 5x^4$

   e $5c^4 \times 4c$

Guided

3 Copy and complete. The first one has been done for you.

   a $4^5 \div 4^3 = \dfrac{\cancel{4} \times \cancel{4} \times \cancel{4} \times 4 \times 4}{\cancel{4} \times \cancel{4} \times \cancel{4}} = 4^2$

   b $5^8 \div 5^5 = \dfrac{\square \times \square \times \square \times \square \times \square \times \square \times \square \times \square}{\square \times \square \times \square \times \square \times \square} = 5^{\square}$

   c $3^4 \div 3$

   d $6^4 \div 6^2$

   e $t^5 \div t^2$

   f $s^3 \div s$

   g Reasoning What do you notice about the answers to parts **a–f**?

4 Simplify

a $10b^4 \div 2b = \dfrac{10\square^4}{2\square}$

$\qquad\qquad\quad = 5\square^\square$

b $8b^5 \div 2b^2$

c $9x^6 \div 3x^4$

d $12a^8 \div 3a^2$

e $10y^3 \div y$

Q4e hint y is the same as $1y^1$

Worked example

Simplify

a $(3^4)^2$

$\qquad (3^4)^2 = 3^4 \times 3^4 = 3^8$

b $(2a^2)^3$

$\qquad (2a^2)^3 = 2a^2 \times 2a^2 \times 2a^2$

$\qquad\qquad\quad = 2 \times 2 \times 2 \times a^2 \times a^2 \times a^2$

$\qquad\qquad\quad = 8a^6$

Multiply the numbers and add the powers together.

Guided

5 Simplify

a $(3^4)^2 = 3^4 \times 3^4 = 3^\square$

b $(5^2)^3 = 5^2 \times 5^\square \times 5^\square = 5^\square$

c $(a^6)^2 = a^\square \times a^\square = a^\square$

d $(x^4)^3 = x^{(4 \times \square)} = x^\square$

e $(4m^3)^2 = 4m^3 \times 4m^3 = \square m^\square$

f $(3p^5)^3 = 3p^5 \times 3p^5 \times 3p^5 = \square p^\square$

Guided

6 Copy and complete this pattern.

$2^3 = 2 \times 2 \times 2 = 8$

$\qquad\qquad\qquad\qquad\Big)\div 2$

$2^2 = 2 \times 2 = \square$

$\qquad\qquad\qquad\qquad\Big)\div 2$

$2^1 = \square$

$\qquad\qquad\qquad\qquad\Big)\div 2$

$2^0 = \square$

---

7 Evaluate

a 10^1 **b** 7^0 **c** 4^2

d 6^0 **e** 3^1 **f** x^0

Collecting like terms involving powers

1 Simplify these expressions. The first two have been done for you.

a $a + a = 2a$ **b** $a^2 + a^2 = 2a^2$

c $a^3 + a^3 = \square a^3$ **d** $b^2 + b^2 + b^2 = \square b^2$

e $x^2 + x^2 + x^2 + x^2 = \square x^2$

> **Key point** a^2 and a^2 are like terms and can be collected and simplified.
> a^3 and a^3 are like terms and can be collected and simplified.

2 Simplify these expressions. The first one has been done for you.

a $4a + 3a = 7a$ **b** $4a^2 + 3a^2 = \square a^2$

c $2a^3 + 3a^3 = \square a^3$ **d** $4b^2 + 2b^2 = \square b^2$

e $3b^2 + b^2 + 2b^2 = \square b^2$

Expanding brackets: grid method

1 Expand the brackets.

a $3(x + 2)$ **b** $4(y + 5)$

c $2(2x + 3)$ **d** $5(4a - 3)$

2 Expand the brackets.

$y(y + 1)$

×	y	+1
y	y^2	$+y$

$= y(y + 1) = \square^2 + \square$

3 Expand the brackets.

a $x(x + 1)$

×	x	+1
x	$\square^2$	$+\square$

$= \square^2 + x$

b $y(y - 3)$

×	y	-3
y	$\square^2$	$-\square$

$= \square^2 - \square y$

c $a(2a + 4)$

×	$2a$	+4
a	$\square$	$+\square$

$= \square a^\square + \square a$

d $p(4p - 3)$

×	$4p$	-3
p	$\square$	$-\square$

$= \square p^\square - \square p$

4 Expand the brackets.

$p(p^2 + 4)$

×	p^2	+4
p	p^3	$+4p$

$p(p^2 + 4) = \square^3 + 4\square$

5 Expand the brackets.

a $p(p^2 + 2)$ **b** $x(x^2 + 3)$ **c** $a(a^2 - 3)$ **d** $y(y^2 - 1)$

Factorising by taking out one term

1 Find the highest common factor of

    a 12 and 4   **b** 20 and 10

> **Key point**   **Factorise** means to 'put back into brackets' by finding a factor common to all the terms. Look for the highest common factor.

> **Worked example**
>
> Factorise $6a + 3b$.
>
> $6a + 3b = 3(2a + b)$
>
> > 3 is the highest common factor of 6 and 3 so write it outside the brackets.
>
> Check: $3(2a + b) = 3 \times 2a + 3 \times b$
> $$= 6a + 3b \checkmark$$
>
> > Check your answer by expanding the brackets.

Guided

2 Copy and complete to factorise these. Check your answers.

    a $4x + 6 = 2(\square x + \square)$

    b $8a + 2 = \square(\square a + \square)$

    c $12b + 4 = \square(\square b + \square)$

    d $20y + 10 = \square(\square y + \square)$

> **Q2c and d hint** Check that you have used the highest common factor.

> **Worked example**
>
> Factorise $x^2 + 2x$
>
> $x^2 + 2x = x(x + 2)$
>
> > As x is the highest common factor of x^2 and x, write it outside the brackets.

Guided

3 Copy and complete to factorise these. Check your answers.

    a $x^2 + 2x = x(x + \square)$

    b $y^2 + 3y = y(y + \square)$

    c $a^2 - 5a = a(a - \square)$

    d $p^2 - 10p = \square(\square - \square)$

    e $2x^2 + 4x = 2x(x + \square)$

    f $3b^2 + 6b = 3b(\square + \square)$

> **Q3e hint** The highest common factor of $2x^2$ and $4x$ is $2x$.

> **Reflect**   In this lesson you expanded, simplified and factorised.
> Explain the difference between expanding, simplifying and factorising.

2.6 Expanding double brackets

> • Multiply out double brackets and collect like terms

Expanding double brackets

1 Use the grid method to work out 23 × 42.

×	20	+3
40	800	+120
+2	+40	+6

= 800 + 120 + 40 + 6 = ☐

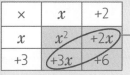

2 Use the grid method to work out 35 × 21.

×	30	+5
20	☐	☐
+1	☐	☐

= ☐ + ☐ + ☐ + ☐ = ☐

Worked example

Expand and simplify $(x + 2)(x + 3)$ using the grid method.

×	x	+2
x	x^2	+2x
+3	+3x	+6

> The diagonal terms are 'like terms' and so can be collected.

$(x + 2)(x + 3)$
$= x^2 + 2x + 3x + 6$
$= x^2 + 5x + 6$

---

3 Copy and complete to expand and simplify $(a + 5)(a + 2)$.

×	a	+5
a	a^2	+5☐
+2	+2☐	+☐

$= a^2 + ☐a + ☐$

4 Expand and simplify

    a $(x + 4)(x + 3)$

    b $(a + 1)(a + 2)$

    c $(a + 5)(a + 3)$

    d $(y + 4)(y + 2)$

5 Expand and simplify

    a $(x + 4)(x - 2)$

> **Q5 hint** Be careful when multiplying by a negative number.

×	x	$+4$
x	x^2	$+4\square$
-2	$-2\square$	$-\square$

    b $(x - 4)(x + 2)$

    c $(x - 4)(x - 2)$

    d Reasoning What do you notice about your answers to parts **a** and **b**?

6 Expand and simplify

    a $(a + 5)(a - 4)$

    b $(p - 3)(p + 2)$

    c $(m - 4)(m - 2)$

7 Expand and simplify

    a $(x + 4)^2 = (x + 4)(x + 4) = $ _____

    b $(y + 2)^2$

    c $(p - 1)^2$

Reflect Gemma expanded and simplified $(x - 3)(x + 6)$.

Her answer was $x^2 - 3x + 18$.

Check her answer. What mistakes did she make?

3 Dealing with data

3.1 Planning a survey

- Identify sources of primary and secondary data
- Choose a suitable sample size and what data to collect
- Identify factors that might affect data collection and plan to reduce bias

Choosing which data to collect

1   Kayla wants to find out whether males or females travel longer distances to work.
    Her survey asks these four questions.

    A What is your age?

    B What is your gender?

    C What is your salary?

    D What distance do you travel to work, in miles?

    a Which question will help her know whether she is speaking to a male or female?

    b Which question will help her know how far they travel to work?

2   Amir wants to find out whether older people earn more money than younger people.
    Which pieces of information from **Q1** should he collect?

> **Q2 hint** Which information will tell Amir how old a person is and which will tell him how much they earn?

3   Abha wants to find out if males earn more money than females.
    Which pieces of information from **Q1** should she collect?

Primary and secondary data

1   Which of these people collected data themselves?

> **Q1 hint** Primary data is data you collect yourself.

    Hannah asked students in her class what they thought of a new TV show.

    Ryan found information about life expectancy using online records.

    Sasha found information about goals scored per football game in the newspaper.

    Tim asked his neighbours what they thought of the new park.

2 Which of these people used data that was collected by someone else?

Q2 hint Secondary data is data collected by someone else.

Lamarr found information about number of cars per household using online records.

Olivia found information about voting using online data.

Ethan asked people at a party about their favourite dessert.

Ruth asked members of her football team about their favourite sports person.

3 Which people in **Q1** and **Q2** used **primary** sources?

4 Which people in **Q1** and **Q2** used **secondary** sources?

Sample size

1 Work out 10% of
  a 500
  b 2000
  c 250
  d 80

2 Choose an appropriate sample size for each situation.

Q2 hint An appropriate sample size is usually 10% of the whole population. Use your answers to **Q1** to help.

  a There are 500 members of a gym. Ismail wants to find out their favourite piece of equipment.
  b There are 2000 people living in a village. Hailey wants to find out the residents' views on the library.
  c There are 250 students in Year 9. Mariah wants to find out what music they should play at an end-of-year dance.
  d There are 80 members of a scout group. Jacob wants to find out what they should do for a group project.

Data collection

1 Josh has some **hypotheses** about the students in his class.

Q1 hint A **hypothesis** is a statement you can test by collecting data.

Hypothesis	Data collection
i 20% of the students in my class were born in September.	A Ask students if they want to go to university.
ii 15% of the students in my class say science is their favourite subject.	B Look at school records about how students travel to school.
iii 85% of the students in my class want to go to university.	C Look at school records about birth month.
iv 30% of the students in my class take the bus to school.	D Ask students to name their favourite subject.

  a Match each hypothesis with the best way of collecting relevant data.
  b Which sources of data are primary sources?

2 Match each measurement with the most appropriate unit of measure.

Q2 hint Shorter distances are usually measured more accurately.

Measurement	Unit of measure
i Distance between two cities	**A** Nearest mm
ii Height	**B** Nearest km
iii Length of finger	**C** Nearest cm

Bias and random samples

1 Reasoning Danny wants to find out what residents of his town think about the new supermarket. He plans to ask the people in his family.

Q1 hint A sample that does not represent the whole population is likely to be **biased**.

  a Explain why Danny's sample will not represent the views of the whole town.

  b Is Danny's sample **biased**? Explain your answer.

2 Reasoning Explain why each of these samples would be biased.

  a Usman asks the first 10 people he sees at school if they think school should start earlier.

  b Becky asks her friends to name their favourite restaurant.

  c Emily asks people in a town centre whether they want a new car park built.

Reflect   Think about the different topics covered in the lesson:
- choosing suitable data
- primary and secondary data
- sample size
- data collection
- biased samples.

Discuss with a partner how you would investigate the number of people in your school with blue eyes. Try to discuss each topic from this lesson.

3.2 Collecting data

- Design and use data collection sheets and tables
- Design a good questionnaire

Discrete and continuous data

1 Reasoning The numbers of emails received in an hour by 15 employees are

  7, 11, 5, 15, 16, 12, 3, 4, 8, 14, 9, 13, 5, 10, 9

a Is it possible to receive 2.3 emails?

b Is this data **discrete**? Explain.

> **Q1b hint** When the data comes from counting items, it can only take whole-number values so it is **discrete**.

2 Reasoning Hugh measures his tomato plants one morning with a ruler. His measurements, in centimetres, are

  5.3, 6.4, 5.6, 6.1, 4.1, 7.3, 4.5, 4.6, 5.7, 5.5

Is this data **continuous**? Explain.

> **Q2 hint Continuous** data is measured. It can take any value in a range.

3 Reasoning At a fairground, the number of people that go on the dodgems each night is recorded. Here are the results.

  267, 350, 337, 343, 290, 328, 317, 178, 342, 259, 372, 169, 304, 233, 266, 297

Is this data discrete or continuous? Explain.

Data collection sheets

> **Key point**   Discrete and continuous data are grouped differently. Decide which type of data you have before beginning to group the data.
> Discrete data will have groups like 0–5, 6–10, 11–15, …
> Continuous data will have groups like $0 < x \leqslant 5$, $5 < x \leqslant 10$, $10 < x \leqslant 15$, …
> There are no gaps between groups in continuous data.

Guided

1 Gavin asked his class to record how many portions of fruit they ate in a week. These are his results.

  21, 16, 4, 16, 17, 1, 9, 0, 11, 23, 12

a Copy and complete the data collection sheet for this data.

Portions of fruit	Portions of fruit (grouped)	Tally	Frequency
0, 1, 2, 3, 4, 5	0–5		
6, 7, 8, 9, 10, 11	6–☐		
12, 13, 14, ☐, ☐, ☐	☐–☐		
18, ☐, ☐, ☐, ☐, ☐	☐–☐		

b Is this data discrete or continuous?

2 Jess records the reaction times, in seconds, for a group of students in her class. These are her results.

0.47, 0.65, 0.18, 0.73, 0.29, 0.56, 0.19, 0.47, 0.41, 0.60

a Copy and complete the data collection sheet for this data.

Reaction times	Tally	Frequency
$0.0 \leqslant x < 0.2$		
$0.2 \leqslant x < 0.4$		
$\square \leqslant x < \square$		
$\square \leqslant x < 0.8$		

b Is this data discrete or continuous?

3 Oliver asked students in his class to record how many days last month they did at least 30 minutes of exercise. These are his results.

14, 6, 9, 1, 7, 22, 17, 19, 10, 13, 9, 2, 18, 6

a Is this data discrete or continuous?

b What is the lowest data value?

c What is the highest data value?

Oliver would like to divide the data into five groups of equal size.

d Suggest rounded values for the beginning and end of your data groups.

e Divide the data into five groups.
Copy and complete the frequency table for the data.

Days	Tally	Frequency

> **Q3e hint** Use the Key point to select the correct way of grouping your data. Check that each data value fits into one of the groups.

4 Mei measures the length in centimetres of the middle finger of 10 students in her class. These are her results.

6.9, 7.8, 6.3, 8.2, 5.8, 7.6, 8.5, 6.6, 7.2, 8.0

a Is this data discrete or continuous?

b What is the lowest data value?

c What is the highest data value?

Mei would like to divide the data into five groups of equal size.

d Suggest rounded values for the beginning and end of your data groups.

e Divide the data into five groups. Draw and complete a frequency table for the data.

Two-way tables

1 The table shows the age and eye colour of five friends.

Name	Age (years)	Eye colour
Adele	23	Blue
Justin	38	Brown
Maddy	31	Blue
Penny	25	Green
Sabir	24	Brown

The data is going to be recorded in this two-way table.

	Eye colour		
Age (years)			

a Write two equal intervals for the age data.

b Write three headings for the eye colour data.

c Copy the two-way table. Write the headings in the correct places.

> **Q1a hint** Age is discrete data, so use the correct notation.

2 The two-way table shows information about year group and height of five students.

Name	Year group	Height (cm)
Abi	9	156
Chen	10	162
Henry	10	167
Nadia	9	153
Sophia	10	159

The data is going to be recorded in this two-way table.

	Year group	
Height (cm)		

a Write two headings for the year group data.

b Write two equal intervals for the height data.

c Copy the two-way table. Write the headings in the correct places.

> **Q2b hint** Height is continuous data, so use the correct notation.

Designing a questionnaire

1 Thomas wants to find out people's views on apples. He has these two possible questions.

> **A** Apples are the best fruit. Do you agree?
>
> ☐ Yes   ☐ No
>
> **B** Do you enjoy eating apples?
>
> ☐ Yes   ☐ No

    a Which question encourages you to pick 'Yes'?

    b Which question should Thomas use?

> **Q1b hint** A question should not lead towards one answer.

2 Megan wants to find out how many hours her friends spend watching TV each week. She has these two possible questions.

> **A** How many hours of TV do you watch each week?
>
> ☐ 0–1
>
> ☐ 2–4
>
> ☐ 5–10
>
> **B** How many hours of TV do you watch each week?
>
> ☐ 0–1
>
> ☐ 3–4
>
> ☐ 6–10

> **Q2 hint** What if one of Megan's friends watches 5 hours of TV each week?

Which question has the better response section?

3 Yusuf wants to find out students' views on the amount of homework they receive. He has these two possible questions.

> **A** How many minutes do you spend on homework each night?
>
> ☐ 0–10
>
> ☐ 11–30
>
> ☐ 31–60
>
> ☐ 61 or more
>
> **B** Do you get too much homework?
>
> ☐ Yes   ☐ No

    a Which question has a vague response section?

    b Which question should Yusuf use?

> **Reflect** Look back at the section on designing a questionnaire. Discuss with a partner some important ideas for designing good questions and good response sections.

3.3 Calculating averages

- Find the median from a frequency table
- Estimate the mean from a large set of grouped data

Calculating the median from a table

Key point

The **median** of n ordered values is the $\frac{n+1}{2}$th value.

For example, if there are 15 values, the median is the $\frac{15+1}{2} = \frac{16}{2} = 8$th value.

1 The table shows the number of siblings for 19 people in a class.

Number of siblings	Frequency
0	6
1	8
2	3
3	2
Total	**19**

a Copy and complete by writing the data in **ascending** order.

0, 0, 0, 0, 0, 0,   1, 1, 1, 1, 1, 1, 1, 1,   2, 2, 2,   3, 3

    6 people have   ☐ people have   ☐ people   ☐ people
    0 siblings   1 sibling   have   have
                                          2 siblings ☐ siblings

> **Q1a hint** Ascending means 'increasing'.

b Copy and complete: The median value is the $\frac{19+1}{2} = \frac{\square}{2} = \square$th value.

c Circle the median value.

d What is the median number of siblings?

2 The table shows the number of computers per household in one street.

Number of computers	Frequency	Running total
0	5	5
1	7	5 + 7 = 12
2	14	12 + 14 = ☐
3	2	☐ + 2 = ☐
4	1	☐ + 1 = ☐
Total	**29**	

a Copy the table and complete the last column.

b Work out which value is the median value.

> **Q2b hint** $\frac{29+1}{2} = \frac{\square}{2}$

c Copy and complete.
  i Houses 1–5 have 0 computers.
  ii Houses 6–12 have ☐ computer.
  iii Houses 13–☐ have 2 computers.
  iv Houses ☐–☐ have 3 computers.
  v House ☐ has 4 computers.

d What is the median number of computers per household?

Calculating the mean from a grouped frequency table

1 Find the midpoint of each class. Some have been started for you.

a $10 \leqslant x < 20$ $\dfrac{10 + 20}{2} = \dfrac{\square}{2} = \square$

b $5 \leqslant x < 10$ $\dfrac{\square + \square}{2} = \dfrac{\square}{2} = \square$

c $15 < x \leqslant 25$ $\dfrac{15 + 25}{2} = \dfrac{\square}{2} = \square$

d $24 < x \leqslant 32$ $\dfrac{\square + \square}{2} = \dfrac{\square}{2} = \square$

e 11−15

f 21−30

2 The table shows the time taken, in seconds, to complete a puzzle.

Time taken, t (seconds)	Frequency	Midpoint of class
$0 \leqslant t < 20$	3	$\dfrac{0 + 20}{2} = \dfrac{20}{2} = 10$
$20 \leqslant t < 40$	15	$\dfrac{20 + 40}{2} = \dfrac{\square}{2} = \square$
$40 \leqslant t < 60$	8	$\dfrac{\square + \square}{2} = \dfrac{\square}{2} = \square$
$60 \leqslant t < 80$	4	$\dfrac{\square + \square}{2} = \dfrac{\square}{2} = \square$
Total	**30**	

Copy the table and complete the midpoint column.

3 The table shows the number of books that some students have read in the last year.

Books, b	Frequency	Midpoint of class	Midpoint × frequency
$0 \leqslant b < 4$	6	$\dfrac{0 + 4}{2} = \dfrac{4}{2} = 2$	$2 \times 6 = \square$
$4 \leqslant b < 8$	4	$\dfrac{4 + 8}{2} = \dfrac{12}{2} = 6$	$6 \times 4 = \square$
$8 \leqslant b < 12$	11	$\dfrac{\square + \square}{2} = \dfrac{\square}{2} = \square$	$\square \times 11 = \square$
$12 \leqslant b < 16$	3	$\dfrac{\square + \square}{2} = \dfrac{\square}{2} = \square$	$\square \times 3 = \square$
$16 \leqslant b < 20$	1	$\dfrac{\square + \square}{2} = \dfrac{\square}{2} = \square$	$\square \times 1 = \square$
Total	**25**		$\square$

a Copy the table and complete the midpoint column.
b Complete the last column by multiplying the midpoint by the frequency.
c Find the total for the last column.
d Write down an estimate for the total number of books read.

> **Q3d hint** The sum of the last column is an estimate for the total number of books read.

4 The table shows the number of minutes a child spent in a bath each day for a month.

Bath time, t (minutes)	Frequency	Midpoint of class	Midpoint × frequency
$0 \leqslant t < 5$	8	$\dfrac{0+5}{2} = \dfrac{5}{2} = 2.5$	$2.5 \times 8 = \square$
$5 \leqslant t < 10$	5		
$10 \leqslant t < 15$	13		
$15 \leqslant t < 20$	4		
Total	30		$\square$

a Copy and complete the table.

b Write down an estimate for the total time spent in the bath.

c Copy and complete:

An estimate for the mean time spent in the bath is $\dfrac{\square}{30} = \square$.

5 The table shows the number of letters, l, in people's first names.

Letters, l	Frequency	Midpoint of class	Midpoint × frequency
0–2	1	$\dfrac{0+2}{2} = \dfrac{2}{2} = \square$	$\square \times 1 = \square$
3–5	14		
6–8	8		
9–11	2		
Total	25		$\square$

a Copy and complete the table.

b Write down an estimate for the total number of letters in people's first names.

c Copy and complete:

An estimate for the mean number of letters in people's first names is $\dfrac{\square}{25} = \square$.

6 a Work out an estimate for the mean number of books in **Q3**.

b **Reasoning** Why is this an estimate? Explain your answer.

Reflect Write a list of steps to calculate the mean from a grouped frequency table.
Compare your list with a partner's.

3.4 Displaying and analysing data

- Construct and use a line of best fit to estimate missing values
- Identify outliers in data
- Identify further lines of enquiry
- Draw graphs to represent grouped data

Outliers and correlation

1   Which scatter graphs contain an **outlier**?

> **Q1 hint** An **outlier** on a scatter graph will be away from the other points because it does not fit the pattern.

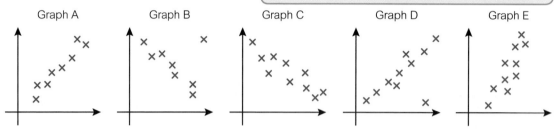

Graph A   Graph B   Graph C   Graph D   Graph E

2   Describe the correlation shown by each graph in **Q1**.

Using lines of best fit to estimate

> **Key point**   The **line of best fit** is a line that best represents the pattern of the data on a scatter graph.

Guided

1   The scatter graph shows the ages of 15 people and the number of hours of sleep they usually get.

> **Q1 hint** Use the arrows on the graph to help.

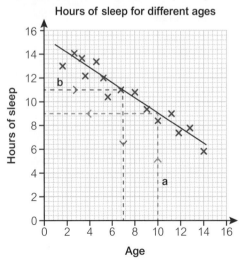

Hours of sleep for different ages

a   Adi is 10 years old. Use the line of best fit to estimate his hours of sleep.
b   Vicky got 11 hours of sleep. Use the line of best fit to estimate her age.

2 For each scatter graph, decide which line of best fit represents the data better.

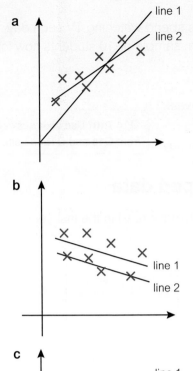

a
line 1
line 2

b
line 1
line 2

c
line 1
line 2

3 The scatter graph shows the time (in minutes) and cost (in £) for 10 different plumbers to repair a dishwasher.

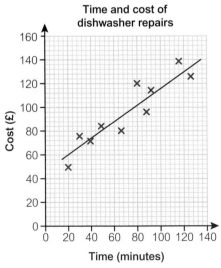

Time and cost of dishwasher repairs

Cost (£)

Time (minutes)

Use the line of best fit to predict
a the cost of a 100-minute repair
b the time taken to do the repair when the cost is £90.

Further enquiry

1 A teacher wants to know how long, on average, students spend watching TV each day. There are 600 students in her school. She asks a random sample of 10 students how long they watch TV for on a Tuesday.

a How many students should the teacher have asked?

b What is wrong with only asking about one day of the week?

c Suggest two ways in which the teacher can further investigate how long students spend watching TV each day.

Q1c hint Use your answers from **Q1a** and **Q1b** to help.

Drawing a line graph to represent grouped data

Guided

1 The table shows the number of books that some students have read in the last year.

Books, b	Frequency	Midpoint of class	Coordinates
$0 \leqslant b < 4$	6	2	(2, 6)
$4 \leqslant b < 8$	4	6	
$8 \leqslant b < 12$	11	10	
$12 \leqslant b < 16$	3	14	
$16 \leqslant b < 20$	1	18	

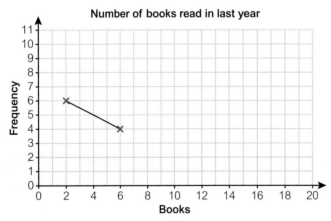

Number of books read in last year

a Copy the axes.

b Copy and complete the coordinate pairs:
(2, 6), (6, 4), (10, ☐), (☐, ☐), (☐, ☐).

c Plot the remaining points onto your graph.

d Join the points with straight lines. The first line has been drawn for you.

Q1b hint The coordinates are (midpoint, frequency). The midpoint is on the x-axis and the frequency is on the y-axis.

2 Find the midpoint of each time interval.

  a 2pm and 4pm

  b 12pm and 1pm

  c 11am and 1pm

  d 1pm and 4pm

Q2 hint Use a number line to help.

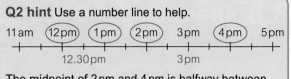

The midpoint of 2pm and 4pm is halfway between 2pm and 4pm.

3 Simon records how many emails he receives each hour one Monday afternoon.

Time	Frequency	Midpoint of class
12pm–1pm	3	12.30pm
1pm–2pm	7	☐
2pm–3pm	9	☐
3pm–4pm	8	☐
4pm–5pm	4	☐

a Copy and complete the table by filling in the midpoint column.

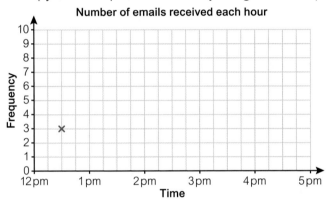

b Copy the axes and plot the data from the table onto the graph. The first point has been plotted for you.

Reflect   Write all the steps needed to draw a line graph for grouped data.
Compare your list with a partner's.

3.5 Presenting and comparing data

- Draw back-to-back stem and leaf diagrams
- Write a report to show survey results

Interpreting charts

1 The bar chart shows the number of games won by two football teams over five seasons.

Copy and complete.

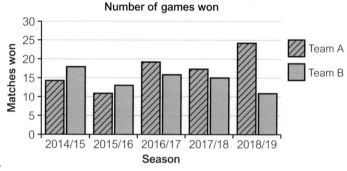

Number of games won

a In 2015/16 team A won ☐ matches.

b In 2014/15 team ☐ won more matches than team ☐.

c In ☐/☐ team ☐ won 24 matches.

The league started in 1990/91 and there are 16 teams in the league.

d What else could you do to investigate these two teams?

e What else could you do to investigate the whole league?

Stem and leaf diagrams

1 Two salespeople in an electrical store recorded how many TVs they sold each week for 15 weeks. The results are shown in the back-to-back stem and leaf diagram.

Salesperson A		Salesperson B
9 ⑥	0	
7 3 2 0	1	② 3 5 5 7 9
8 8 5 2 ①	2	1 ⑧ 9
③ 3 0	3	0 2 2 5 9
2 1 1	4	③

Key 3 | 1 means 13   2 | 8 means 28

a Write the numbers that the ringed values represent, from smallest to largest.

Q1a hint Use the key to help read the diagram. For salesperson A, 3 | 1 means 13.

b Look at the side for salesperson A.

i Work out $\frac{15 + 1}{2}$. Count up the values in the stem and leaf diagram starting from the smallest until you reach this value. This is their median number of TVs sold.

ii What was the minimum number of TVs sold? This is the lowest number for salesperson A.

iii What was the maximum number of TVs sold?

iv Copy and complete to find the range: maximum number − minimum number = ☐ − ☐ = ☐

c For salesperson B, write

i the median number of TVs sold

ii the minimum number of TVs sold

iii the maximum number of TVs sold

iv the range of TVs sold.

2 A class were shown a list of 30 words and then shown 30 pictures. They wrote down how many they remembered. These are the results.

Words: 17, 7, 18, 15, 10, 9, 10, 22, 12, 28, 17

Pictures: 28, 8, 22, 26, 13, 6, 20, 26, 10, 30, 14

a Copy the stem and leaf diagram.
Complete the right-hand side, showing Words.
The first few have been done for you.

b Copy and complete:

  i The range of words remembered
   is 28 − 7 = ☐

  ii The median number of words
   remembered is ☐.

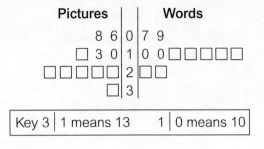

Key 3 | 1 means 13   1 | 0 means 10

c Complete the left-hand side, showing Pictures. The first few have been done for you.

d For Pictures, work out

  i the range   **ii** the median.

> **Q2a and c hint** Rewrite the list of results for words and pictures in order so you don't miss any when writing them into the stem and leaf diagram.

Writing a report

1 Two people collected money for charity.
They recorded the number of donations every 10 minutes for one hour. person A stood on a main road and person B was on a side street.
The table shows the results.

Time (minutes)	0	10	20	30	40	50	60
Donations given to person A	0	18	39	46	67	82	107
Donations given to person B	0	7	21	30	34	45	58

a Copy and complete the line graph showing the number of donations each person received.

Lakshmi suggests this hypothesis:

People collecting on main roads receive more donations than people collecting on side streets.

Write a report using the prompts below.

b What do the results show?
The results show that _____ collected more donations than _____.

c Do the results support Lakshmi's hypothesis?
These results support / do not support Lakshmi's hypothesis.

d How could Lakshmi investigate further?
Lakshmi could improve this study by collecting data for a _____ time period, collecting data on _____ days or investigating _____ locations.

Number of donations received

[graph: Donations (y-axis, 0 to 120) vs Time (minutes) (x-axis, 0 to 60), with person A and person B lines plotted]

Key   —— person A   —— person B

> **Reflect**   In the section on writing a report, information was given in a table and on a graph. Which do you find easier to read? Explain your answer. Compare your answer with a partner.

4 Multiplicative reasoning

4.1 Enlargement

- Enlarge 2D shapes using a positive whole number scale factor and a centre of enlargement
- Find the centre of enlargement by drawing lines on a grid
- Understand that the scale factor is the ratio of corresponding lengths

Enlarging a shape by a scale factor about a centre of enlargement

1 Marco enlarges triangle ABC.
He uses a scale factor of 3, with point × as the centre of enlargement.
He labels his enlarged triangle A'B'C'.

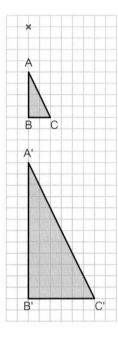

a i How many times longer is A'B' than AB?

ii How many times longer is B'C' than BC?

iii How many times longer is A'C' than AC?

b Copy and complete.
If you enlarge a shape by a scale factor of 3, the sides will all be ☐ times longer.

c Count the squares across and down from
i × to A and × to A'　**ii** × to B and × to B'　**iii** × to C and × to C'.

d Copy and complete.
To enlarge a shape by a scale factor of 3, make each vertex of the enlarged shape ☐ times the distance from the centre of enlargement.

2 Follow these steps to enlarge rectangle ABCD. Use a scale factor of 2, with point × as the centre of enlargement.

a Copy the shape and centre of enlargement onto squared paper.

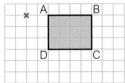

b Write how many squares it is across right or across right and down from × to each vertex of the shape. The first one has been done for you.

i × to A　　2 squares across right

ii × to B　　☐ squares across right

iii × to C　　☐ squares across right, ☐ squares down

iv × to D　　☐ squares across right, ☐ squares down

c To find the position of the enlargement A'B'C'D', multiply all the distances in part **b** by a scale factor of 2. The first one has been done for you.

i ✗ to A' 2 × 2 = 4 squares across right

ii ✗ to B' 6 × 2 = ☐ squares across right

iii ✗ to C' ☐ × 2 = ☐ squares across right, ☐ × 2 = ☐ squares down

iv ✗ to D' ☐ × 2 = ☐ squares across right, ☐ × 2 = ☐ squares down

d Mark the points A', B', C', D' on the diagram and draw lines between them.

e Check:
Is length A'B' = AB × 2?
Is length B'C' = BC × 2?
Is length C'D' = CD × 2?
Is length A'D' = AD × 2?

3 Follow these steps to enlarge triangle ABC. Use a scale factor of 3, with point ✗ as the centre of enlargement.

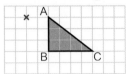

a Copy the shape and centre of enlargement ✗ onto squared paper.

b Copy and complete these tables.

For ABC	
Vertex	**Distance from ✗**
A	2 right
B	2 right, 3 down
C	6 right, ☐ down

For A'B'C'	
Vertex	**Distance from ✗**
A'	2 × 3 = ☐ right
B'	2 × ☐ = ☐ right, 3 × ☐ = ☐ down
C'	6 × ☐ = ☐ right, ☐ × ☐ = ☐ down

c Mark the new vertices A', B', C' on the diagram and draw lines between them.

d Check that all lengths of triangle A'B'C' are 3 times the lengths of the corresponding sides of triangle ABC.

4 **Reasoning** Ali is asked to enlarge the shaded square using a scale factor of 2, with point ✗ as the centre of enlargement.

> **Q4 hint** You could draw tables, as in **Q3**, to help you.

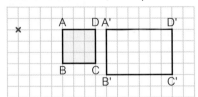

a Explain how you know that Ali has made a mistake.

b Which two vertices are in the wrong positions?

c Copy the shaded square, with centre of enlargement ✗, onto squared paper.

d Enlarge square ABCD. Use a scale factor of 2 and point ✗ as the centre of enlargement.

Finding the scale factor and centre of enlargement

1 The smaller rectangle has been enlarged to make the larger rectangle.

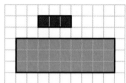

   a What is the height of the smaller rectangle?
   b What is the height of the larger rectangle?
   c Calculate: height of larger rectangle ÷ height of smaller rectangle.
   d What is the scale factor of the enlargement?
   e Check that the length of the larger shape is the length of smaller shape × scale factor.

Worked example

Describe the enlargement that takes shape **M** onto shape **N**.

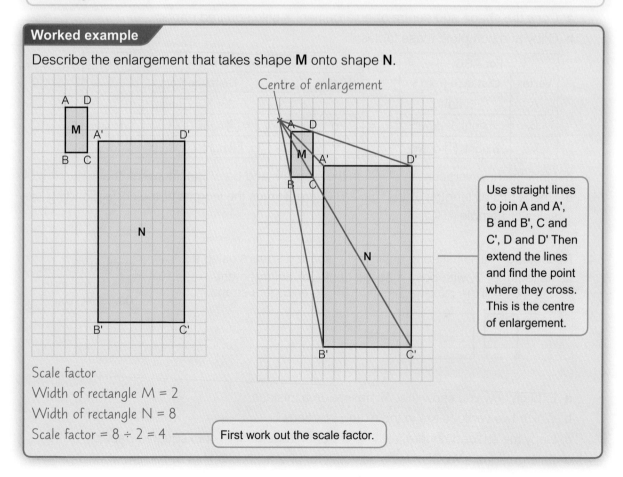

Centre of enlargement

Use straight lines to join A and A', B and B', C and C', D and D' Then extend the lines and find the point where they cross. This is the centre of enlargement.

Scale factor

Width of rectangle M = 2

Width of rectangle N = 8

Scale factor = 8 ÷ 2 = 4 ——— First work out the scale factor.

2 **a** Copy shapes M and N onto squared paper.

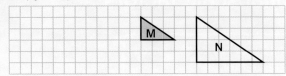

b Work out the scale factor of enlargement.

Q2b hint Work out
height of triangle N ÷ height of triangle M

c Label the vertices of shape M as ABC, and
the corresponding vertices on the enlarged
shape as A'B'C'.

d Use straight lines to join A to A', B to B' and C to C'.

e Extend the lines so that they cross.

f The point where they cross is the centre of enlargement. Mark this point with ×.

3 Copy each pair of shapes onto squared paper.
For each pair find

Q3 hint Follow the method in **Q2**.

a the scale factor

b the centre of enlargement.

i

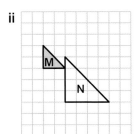

ii

Reflect   List all the information you need to enlarge a shape.

4.2 Negative and fractional scale factors

- Enlarge 2D shapes using a negative whole number scale factor
- Enlarge 2D shapes using a fractional scale factor

Negative scale factors of enlargement

Key point When the scale factor is **negative**, multiply the distance from the centre of enlargement by the scale factor, but plot corresponding vertices in the **opposite** direction, that is, on the other side of the centre of enlargement.

1 Follow the steps to enlarge triangle ABC.
Use a scale factor of −2, with point × as the centre of enlargement.

  a Copy and complete.
  From the centre of enlargement × to
    i A   1 square right, 1 square up
    ii B   ☐ squares right, 1 square up
    iii C   ☐ square right, ☐ squares up

  b Copy and complete.
  Vertices of the enlargement will be
    i A'   2 squares left, 2 squares down
    ii B'   ☐ squares left, ☐ squares down
    iii C'   ☐ squares ...., ☐ squares down

Q1b hint The scale factor is −2.
Multiply each distance in **Q1a** by 2.
Then change it to the opposite direction.

  c Draw the enlargement.

2 Follow these steps to enlarge rectangle ABCD.
Use a scale factor of −1, with point × as the centre of enlargement.

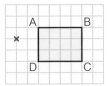

  a Copy the rectangle and the centre of enlargement × onto squared paper.

Q2b hint For the enlarged shape, remember to change the directions from right and up/down to left and down/up.

  b Copy and complete the tables.

For original shape	
Vertex	Distance from ×
A	2 right, 1 up
B	6 right, ☐ up
C	☐ right, ☐ down
D	☐ right, ☐ down

For enlargement	
Vertex	Distance from ×
A'	2 × 1 = 2 left, 1 × ☐ = ☐ down
B'	6 × ☐ = ☐ left, ☐ × ☐ = ☐ down
C'	☐ left, ☐ up
D'	☐ ...., ☐ ....

  c Draw the enlargement on your diagram.

47

3 a Look at the diagram you drew for **Q1**. How much longer are the sides of the triangle in the enlargement than the original triangle?

b How does this relate to the scale factor?

c Look at the diagram you drew for **Q2**. What do you notice about the lengths of the sides of the enlargement compared with the original shape?

d How does this relate to the scale factor?

Fractional scale factors of enlargement

1 Follow the steps to enlarge rectangle ABCD.
Use a scale factor of $\frac{1}{2}$, with point ×
as the centre of enlargement.

a Copy the diagram onto squared paper.

b Copy and complete.
From the centre of enlargement × to

   i A   8 squares right, 6 squares up

   iii C   ☐ squares right, ☐ squares up

   ii B   ☐ squares right, ☐ squares up

   iv D   ☐ squares right, ☐ squares up

c Copy and complete.
Vertices of the enlargement will be

> **Q1c hint** Multiplying by $\frac{1}{2}$ is the same as dividing by 2.

   i A' $8 \times \frac{1}{2} = 4$ squares right, $6 \times \frac{1}{2} = 3$ squares up

   ii B' $\square \times \frac{1}{2} = \square$ squares right, $\square \times \frac{1}{2} = \square$ squares up

   iii C' $\square \times \square = \square$ squares right, $\square \times \square = \square$ squares up

   iv D' $\square \times \square = \square$ squares right, $\square \times \square = \square$ squares up

d Draw the enlargement.

2 Follow these steps to enlarge triangle ABC.
Use a scale factor of $\frac{1}{3}$ and point × as the centre of enlargement.

a Copy the diagram onto squared paper.

b Copy and complete the tables.

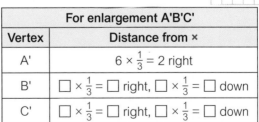

For original shape ABC	
Vertex	Distance from ×
A	6 right
B	☐ right, ☐ down
C	☐ right, ☐ down

For enlargement A'B'C'	
Vertex	Distance from ×
A'	$6 \times \frac{1}{3} = 2$ right
B'	$\square \times \frac{1}{3} = \square$ right, $\square \times \frac{1}{3} = \square$ down
C'	$\square \times \frac{1}{3} = \square$ right, $\square \times \frac{1}{3} = \square$ down

c Draw the enlargement.

4.3 Percentage change

- Find an original value using inverse operations
- Calculate percentage change

Finding the original value

1 In a sale, prices are reduced to 75% of the original price.

   a Tim calculates 75% of £350 like this:

Original price ⟶ ×75% ⟶ Sale price

£350 ⟶ ×0.75 ⟶ ?

   What is the sale price?

   b Tim finds an item in the sale with a price of £300. He wants to know the original price. He works it out like this:

Original price ⟵ ÷75% ⟵ Sale price

? ⟵ ÷0.75 ⟵ £300

   What was the original price?

2 In another sale, prices are reduced to 45% of the original price.

   a Work out the sale prices for items that had these original prices.

£60   £21   £240

Q2a hint

Original price ⟶ ×0.45 ⟶ Sale price

   b Work out the sale prices for items that had these original prices.

    i £180   **ii** £440   **iii** £290

   c Work out the original prices of items with these sale prices.

    i £16.20   **ii** £20.25   **iii** £45

Q2c hint Read the question carefully. This time you are asked to find the original price, **before** the sale discount (reduction) is applied.

3 The price of a car has dropped by 20%. Its current price is £25 000.

   a What percentage of the original price is the car's current price?

   b Copy and complete to work out the original price of the car.

Q3a hint
100% − 20% = ☐%

Original price ⟵ ÷0.80 ⟵ Current price

? ⟵ ÷☐ ⟵ £25 000

4 **Reasoning** A school reduces its fuel bills by 15%. The new fuel bills are £17 000 per year. Martina is working out the fuel bill for the previous year.

100% − 15% = 85%

85% of £17 000 = 0.85 × 17 000

= £14 450

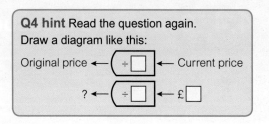

Q4 hint Read the question again. Draw a diagram like this:

Original price ← (÷ ☐) ← Current price

? ← (÷ ☐) ← £☐

a How do you know that this answer must be wrong?

b What has Martina done incorrectly?

c Work out the correct fuel bill for the previous year.

Calculating percentage change

> **Worked example**
>
> Eric's height increases from 120 cm to 126 cm. Work out the percentage change in his height.
>
> Percentage change = $\frac{\text{actual change}}{\text{original amount}}$ × 100
>
> Actual change in height = 126 − 120 = 6 cm —— **Work out the actual change.**
>
> Original height = 120 cm
>
> Percentage change = $\frac{6}{120}$ × 100 —— **Substitute the actual change and original height into the formula.**
>
> = 5%

1 The price of a laptop increases from £500 to £600.

a What is the actual change in price?

b Copy and complete: percentage change = $\frac{\square}{500}$ × 100 = ☐

Q1a hint How much has the price increased by?

2 One week Nikki runs 5 km in 45 minutes. The next week she runs 5 km in 36 minutes.

a What is the actual change in time?

b What was Nikki's original time?

c Copy and complete: percentage change = $\frac{\square}{\square}$ × 100 = ☐

Q2b hint Did she run 5 km in 45 minutes or 5 km in 36 minutes first?

3 **Reasoning** In a sale a TV is reduced from £620 to £500. Ethan is calculating the percentage change.

£620 − £500 = £120

Percentage change = $\frac{120}{500}$ × 100 = 24%

a Explain what he has done wrong.

b Calculate the percentage change correctly. Give your answer to the nearest whole percentage.

> **Reflect** Look back at the calculations you have done to answer questions in this lesson. Have you shown all the steps in your working clearly so that you can check for mistakes? How can you improve your working or its layout?

4.4 Compound measures

- Solve problems using compound measures
- Solve problems using constant rates and related formulae

Speed, distance and time

Key point **Speed** is a **compound measure** because it combines measures of two different quantities (distance and time).
To calculate speed, use the formula
$$\text{speed} = \frac{\text{distance}}{\text{time}}$$
Common units of measure for speed are km/h (kilometres per hour) and mph (miles per hour).

1 Use the formula to calculate each speed.

   a A runner runs 25 km in 2 hours.   speed = $\dfrac{\square}{2}$ = $\square$ km/h

> **Q1a hint** Speed is in km/h because the distance is in km and the time is in hours.

   b A car travels 120 miles in 3 hours   speed = $\dfrac{\square}{3}$ = $\square$ mph

   c A snail crawls 10 cm in 5 minutes.   speed = $\dfrac{\square}{\square}$ = $\square$ cm/min

2 **a** The formula for speed can be rearranged to calculate distance. Which is the correct rearrangement?

         distance = speed × time   distance = $\dfrac{\text{speed}}{\text{time}}$ distance = $\dfrac{\text{time}}{\text{speed}}$

   b Work out the distance travelled by a car travelling at 70 mph for 3 hours. Make sure you include the units.

> **Q2b hint** The speed is given in miles per hour so the distance will be in ....

3 Lorna cycles at 20 mph.

   a How far does she travel in 1 hour?

   b Copy and complete to find out how long it takes Lorna to travel

     i 40 miles

          ×2 (20 miles : 1 hour) ×☐
              40 miles : ☐ hours

     ii 100 miles

          ×☐ (20 miles : 1 hour) ×☐
              100 miles : ☐ hours

     iii 30 miles

          ×☐ (20 miles : 1 hour) ×☐
              30 miles : ☐ hours

> **Q3biii hint** 20 × ☐ = 30. You can use a calculator and the inverse of multiplication to help you.

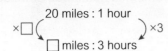

4 Johan drives at 20 mph.
Copy and complete to find out how far Johan travels in

    a 3 hours   **b** 4 hours   **c** 2.5 hours

                 20 miles : 1 hour   20 miles : 1 hour   20 miles : 1 hour

    ×☐ (   ) ×3   ×☐ (   ) ×☐   ×☐ (   ) ×☐

         ☐ miles : 3 hours   ☐ miles : 4 hours   ☐ miles : 2.5 hours

5 The speed of a world-class male sprinter is approximately 10 m/s. Convert this speed to km/h using these steps.

    a How many metres would he run in 1 minute?

> **Q5a hint**   10 metres : 1 second
>   ×☐ (   ) ×☐
>   ☐ metres : 60 seconds
>   (1 minute)

    b How many metres would he run in 1 hour?

> **Q5b hint**   ☐ metres : 1 minute
>   ×☐ (   ) ×☐
>   ☐ metres : ☐ minutes
>   (1 hour)

    c How many km is this?

> **Q5c hint**   ☐ metres
>   ÷1000 (
>   ☐ kilometres

    d Write his speed in km/h.

    e Reasoning Look at your answer to part **b**. Why wouldn't this happen in real life?

6 Copy and complete to convert each speed into km/h.

    a 4 m/s   **b** 200 m/s   **c** 35 m/s

) ×60   ) ×60

    = ☐ m/min   = ☐ m/min   = ☐ m/min

) ×60   ) ×☐

    = ☐ m/h   = ☐ m/h   = ☐ m/h

) ÷1000   ) ÷☐

    = ☐ km/h   = ☐ km/h   = ☐ km/h

7 Copy and complete to convert each speed into m/s.

> **Q7 hint** Round your answers to the nearest whole number.

    a 50 km/h   **b** 120 km/h   **c** 80 km/h

) ×1000   ) ×1000

    = ☐ m/h   = ☐ m/h   = ☐ m/h

) ÷60   ) ÷60

    = ☐ m/min   = ☐ m/min   = ☐ m/min

) ÷60   ) ÷60

    = ☐ m/s   = ☐ m/s   = ☐ m/s

Density, mass and volume

1 Use the formula to calculate each density.

> **Q1 hint** In these questions density is measured in grams per cm³ because the mass is given in grams and the volume in cm³.

   a A block has mass 200 g and volume 20 cm³.   density $= \dfrac{\square}{20} = \square$ g/cm³

   b A gold ring has mass 10 g and volume 0.5 cm³.   density $= \dfrac{\square}{\square} = \square$ g/cm³

   c A lead pipe has mass 56 g and volume 7 cm³.   density $= \dfrac{\square}{\square} = \square$ g/cm³

2 A material with a density of 1.2 g/cm³ has a mass of 1.2 g for every 1 cm³ of volume.
   Copy and complete to find out the mass for a volume of

   a 2 cm³   **b** 10 cm³   **c** 3.5 cm³

   $\times\square \Big(\overset{1.2\,\text{g}\,:\,1\,\text{cm}^3}{\underset{\square\,\text{g}\,:\,2\,\text{cm}^3}{}} \Big) \times\square$ $\times\square \Big(\overset{1.2\,\text{g}\,:\,1\,\text{cm}^3}{\underset{\square\,\text{g}\,:\,10\,\text{cm}^3}{}} \Big) \times\square$ $\times\square \Big(\overset{1.2\,\text{g}\,:\,1\,\text{cm}^3}{\underset{\square\,\text{g}\,:\,3.5\,\text{cm}^3}{}} \Big) \times\square$

> **Q2 hint** The density is given in grams per cm³ so the mass will be in ....

3 A copper disc has density 9 g/cm³.
   Copy and complete to work out the volume when the mass is
   a 18 g   **b** 4.5 g   **c** 3 g

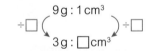

   $\times\square \Big(\overset{9\,\text{g}\,:\,1\,\text{cm}^3}{\underset{18\,\text{g}\,:\,\square\,\text{cm}^3}{}} \Big) \times\square$ $\div\square \Big(\overset{9\,\text{g}\,:\,1\,\text{cm}^3}{\underset{4.5\,\text{g}\,:\,\square\,\text{cm}^3}{}} \Big) \div\square$ $\div\square \Big(\overset{9\,\text{g}\,:\,1\,\text{cm}^3}{\underset{3\,\text{g}\,:\,\square\,\text{cm}^3}{}} \Big) \div\square$

> **Q3 hint** The density is given in grams per cm³ so the volume will be in ....

Pressure, force and area

1 Use the formula to calculate each pressure.

   a A force of $20\,N$ is applied to an area of $20\,cm^2$.

   pressure $= \dfrac{\square}{20} = \square\ N/cm^2$

   b A force of $5\,N$ is applied to an area of $20\,cm^2$.

   pressure $= \dfrac{\square}{\square} = \square\ N/cm^2$

   c A force of $50\,N$ is applied to an area of $2\,cm^2$.

   pressure $= \dfrac{\square}{\square} = \square\ N/cm^2$

> **Q1 hint** In these questions pressure is measured in N/cm^2 because the force is measured in newtons (N) and the area in cm^2.

2 A pressure of $200\,N/cm^2$ means that $200\,N$ is applied to each $1\,cm^2$.
Copy and complete to work out the force applied to an area of

   a $2\,cm^2$

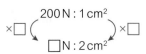

> **Q2 hint** The pressure is given in N/cm^2 so the force will be in ....

   b $12\,cm^2$

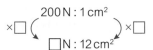

   c $0.5\,cm^2$

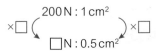

3 The pressure applied to a surface is $5\,N/cm^2$.
Copy and complete to work out the area of the surface when the force applied is

   a $20\,N$

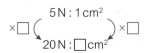

> **Q3 hint** The pressure is given in N/cm^2 so the area will be in ....

   b $55\,N$

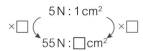

   c $2.5\,N$

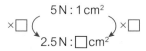

Reflect Look back at the first Key point in this lesson. Which of these are compound measures? Explain.

   litres   miles per hour   £/day   kilograms

4.5 Direct and inverse proportion

- Solve best-buy problems
- Solve problems involving inverse proportion

Direct proportion

1 **a** A taxi charges £13.00 for a 10-mile journey.
Copy and complete the calculation to work out the cost of a 7-mile journey.

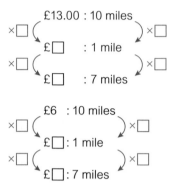

£13.00 : 10 miles
×☐ ( ) ×☐
£☐ : 1 mile
×☐ ( ) ×☐
£☐ : 7 miles

b A bus charges £6 for a 10-mile journey.
Work out the cost of a 7-mile journey on the bus.

£6 : 10 miles
×☐ ( ) ×☐
£☐ : 1 mile
×☐ ( ) ×☐
£☐ : 7 miles

c **Problem-solving**   How much more does it cost to travel 10 miles by taxi than by bus?

d **Reasoning**   Charley is working out how much a 5-mile journey will cost by taxi.
She calculates: £13.00 ÷ 2 = £6.50
Explain why she divides by 2.

2 Complete the calculations to work out the cost of

a 1 can   £2.70 ÷ 6 = £☐

b 2 cans   £☐ × ☐ = £☐

c 5 cans   £☐ × ☐ = £☐

d 3 cans   £☐ × ☐ = £☐

e **Reasoning**   Could you work out the cost of 3 cans using a different method?

> **Q2e hint** 3 is $\frac{1}{2}$ of 6.

6 cans £2.70

3 In a shop a multipack of 8 bags of crisps costs £2.80.
Another pack of 12 bags of crisps costs £4.20.
Which is better value for money?

> **Q3 hint** Work out the cost of 1 bag in each pack.

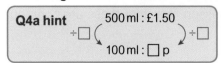

8 bags : £2.80
÷☐ ( ) ÷☐
1 bag : ☐ p

12 bags : £4.20
÷☐ ( ) ÷☐
1 bag : ☐ p

4 Orange juice is sold in two sizes, large and small.

a Work out how much 100 ml of juice costs in

  i the large bottle   **ii** the small bottle.

> **Q4a hint**
> 500 ml : £1.50
> ÷☐ ( ) ÷☐
> 100 ml : ☐ p

Large 500 ml £1.50

Small 300 ml £1.20

Orange Juice

Orange Juice

b Which size is better value for money?

Inverse proportion

1 It takes 1 person 6 hours to paint the lines on a football pitch.

   a Will it take more or less time if 2 people paint the lines?

   b Copy and complete to work out how long it will take

     i 2 people = 6 ÷ 2 = ☐ hours

     ii 3 people = 6 ÷ ☐ = ☐ hours

     iii 6 people = 6 ÷ ☐ = ☐ hour

> **Key point**   Two quantities are in **inverse proportion** if one increases when the other decreases.

2 **Problem-solving** It takes Henry 1 hour to wash 1 car.

   a How long will it take if Rhian helps him?

   b How long will it take if Rhian and Jamel both help him?

> **Q2 hint** Think logically – will it take more or less time?

> **Key point**   If two quantities are in inverse proportion, when you divide one quantity you multiply the other.

3 It takes 3 builders 4 hours to build a wall.

Copy and complete the calculation to work out how long it will take 1 builder.

Number of builders : Time (hours)

$$\div 3 \left(\begin{array}{c} 3:4 \\ \\ 1:\square \end{array} \right) \times 3$$

4 It takes 4 mechanics 2 hours to repair a coach.

Complete the calculations to work out how long it will take

   a 2 mechanics

     Number of : Time
     mechanics (hours)

$$\div 2 \left(\begin{array}{c} 4:2 \\ \\ 2:\square \end{array} \right) \times \square$$

   b 1 mechanic

     Number of : Time
     mechanics (hours)

$$\div \square \left(\begin{array}{c} 4:2 \\ \\ 1:\square \end{array} \right) \times \square$$

   c 8 mechanics

     Number of : Time
     mechanics (hours)

$$\times \square \left(\begin{array}{c} 4:2 \\ \\ 8:\square \end{array} \right) \div \square$$

> **Reflect**   Explain to a classmate how you use multiplication and division when working with direct and inverse proportion. You could look back at a question and explain what you did to answer it.

5 Constructions

5.1 Using scales

- Using scales on maps and diagrams
- Draw diagrams to scale

Reading scale drawings

Guided

1 On a scale drawing 1 cm represents 4 m.

Copy and complete this number line to show some distances in centimetres and the distances they represent in metres.

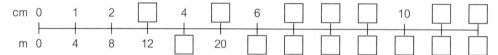

cm 0   1   2   ☐   4   ☐   6   ☐   ☐   ☐   10   ☐   ☐

m   0   4   8   12 ☐   20 ☐   ☐   ☐   ☐   ☐   ☐   ☐

Guided

2 A map uses a scale where 1 cm represents 2 km.

Work out the real-life distance for each measurement on the map.

a 5 cm

$\times 5 \left(\begin{array}{c} 1\,\text{cm} : 2\,\text{km} \\ 5\,\text{cm} : \square\,\text{km} \end{array} \right) \times 5$

b 10 cm

$\times \square \left(\begin{array}{c} 1\,\text{cm} : 2\,\text{km} \\ 10\,\text{cm} : \square\,\text{km} \end{array} \right) \times \square$

c 8 cm

$\times \square \left(\begin{array}{c} 1\,\text{cm} : 2\,\text{km} \\ 8\,\text{cm} : \square\,\text{km} \end{array} \right) \times \square$

d 25 cm

$\times \square \left(\begin{array}{c} 1\,\text{cm} : 2\,\text{km} \\ 25\,\text{cm} : \square\,\text{km} \end{array} \right) \times \square$

Guided

3 A map uses a scale where 1 cm represents 5 km.

Work out the measurement on the map for each real-life distance.

a 10 km

$\times 2 \left(\begin{array}{c} 1\,\text{cm} : 5\,\text{km} \\ \square\,\text{cm} : 10\,\text{km} \end{array} \right) \times 2$

b 20 km

$\times \square \left(\begin{array}{c} 1\,\text{cm} : 5\,\text{km} \\ \square\,\text{cm} : 20\,\text{km} \end{array} \right) \times \square$

c 25 km

$\times \square \left(\begin{array}{c} 1\,\text{cm} : 5\,\text{km} \\ \square\,\text{cm} : 25\,\text{km} \end{array} \right) \times \square$

d 50 km

$\times \square \left(\begin{array}{c} 1\,\text{cm} : 5\,\text{km} \\ \square\,\text{cm} : 50\,\text{km} \end{array} \right) \times \square$

4 This map uses a scale where 1 cm represents 50 m in real life.

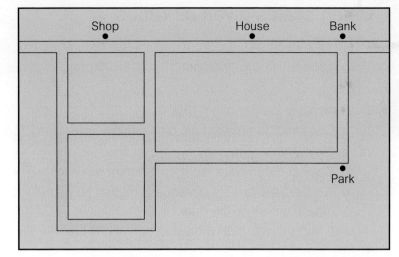

a Measure the distances on the map between

    i the house and the shop

    ii the house and the bank

    iii the bank and the park.

b Work out the real-life distances between

  i the house and the shop   **ii** the house and the bank   **iii** the bank and the park.

 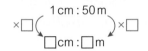 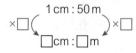

> **Q4bi hint** The bottom left-hand number is your answer from part **a**.

c **Problem-solving** Kosum leaves his house, walks to the bank and then to the park. How far does he walk in total?

Drawing diagrams to scale

1 This is a sketch of a primary school's grounds. The head teacher wants to make a scale drawing using a scale of 1 cm to 10 m.

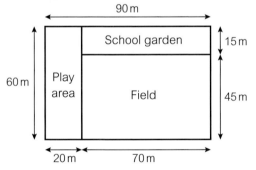

> **Q1a hint** Copy the diagram. As you work out the drawing measurements, write them on your diagram.

a Work out the drawing measurement for each real-life distance.

  i 90 m   **ii** 60 m   **iii** 15 m

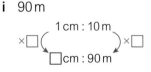 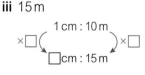

  iv 45 m   **v** 70 m   **vi** 20 m

b Use these steps to create an accurate scale drawing on centimetre squared paper.

  i Draw the large rectangle showing the whole grounds.

  ii Draw and label the play area.

  iii Draw and label the field.

  iv Label the school garden.

Using scales given as ratios

1 Convert each distance from centimetres to metres.

  a 100 cm   b 1000 cm   c 10 000 cm

Q1 hint To convert from centimetres to metres, divide by 100.

Guided

2 A map has a scale of 1 : 10 000.

  a Copy and complete: 1 cm on the map represents ☐ cm in real life.
  b 10 000 cm = ☐ m
  c Copy and complete: 1 cm on the map represents ☐ m in real life.
  d Work out the real-life distance in metres for each measurement on the map.

    i 4 cm   ii 5 cm   iii 10 cm   iv 20 cm

Q2di hint Use a diagram to help.

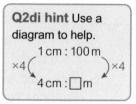

3 Convert each distance from centimetres to metres.

  a 200 cm   b 2000 cm   c 20 000 cm   d 200 000 cm

Q3 hint To convert from centimetres to metres, divide by 100.

Guided

4 A map has a scale of 1 : 20 000.

  a Copy and complete: 1 cm on the map represents ☐ cm in real life.
  b 20 000 cm = ☐ m
  c Copy and complete: 1 cm on the map represents ☐ m in real life.
  d Work out the real-life distance in metres for each measurement on the map.

    i 4 cm   ii 5 cm   iii 10 cm   iv 20 cm

  e Convert your answers to part **d** to kilometres.

Q4di hint Use a diagram to help.
1 cm : 200 m
×4 ( ) ×4
4 cm : ☐ m

Q4e hint To convert from metres to kilometres, divide by 1000.

Guided

5 A map has a scale of 1 : 2500.

  a Copy and complete: 1 cm on the map represents ☐ cm in real life = ☐ m.
  b What distance in metres does 4 cm on the map represent?

  c What distance on the map represents a real-life distance of 400 m?

Reflect   The scale on a map is 1 : 40 000. The distance between the school and the shop on the map is 5 cm. You want to know the real-life distance in metres. Write down the steps needed to solve the problem. Discuss your steps with a partner.

5.2 Basic constructions

• Make accurate constructions using drawing equipment

Drawing a circle

1 a Open your compasses to 6 cm.
   b Draw a dot in the centre of your page.
   c Place the point of your compasses on the dot and draw a circle.
   d Draw a line from the dot to the edge of the circle.
   e Label the line 'radius 6 cm'.

2 Draw a circle with a radius of 9 cm.

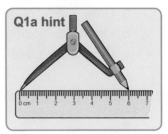

Q1a hint

Q2 hint First open your compasses to 9 cm.

Constructing a perpendicular bisector

Key point   **Perpendicular** lines are at right angles to each other.

1 Which of these pairs of lines are perpendicular?

  a   **b**   **c**   **d**

Key point   A **line bisector** cuts a line in half.

2 a Which of these lines have a bisector?

  i   **ii**   **iii**   **iv**

  b Which of the lines in **Q2a** has a perpendicular bisector?

3 Follow these steps to draw a circle.
  a Draw a straight line of length 12 cm.
  b Draw a circle with its centre at one end of the line.

a
12 cm

b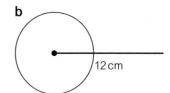
12 cm

Guided

4 Follow these steps to draw a circle of radius 7 cm.

a

10 cm

b

c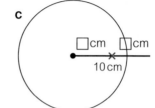

10 cm

a Draw a straight line of length 10 cm.

b Open your compasses to 7 cm.

c Draw a circle with its centre at one end of the line.

5 Follow these steps to draw a circle.

a

10 cm

b ☐ cm   ☐ cm

10 cm

c ☐ cm   ☐ cm

10 cm

a Draw a straight line of length 10 cm.

b What is half of the length of the line?

c Draw a circle with a radius greater than half of the length of the line. The centre of the circle should be one end of the line.

6 Follow these steps to bisect a line.

a

8 cm

b 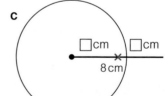 ☐ cm   ☐ cm

8 cm

c ☐ cm   ☐ cm

8 cm

d ☐ cm   ☐ cm

8 cm

e ☐ cm   ☐ cm

8 cm

a Draw a straight line of length 8 cm.

b Open your compasses so that they are greater than half of the length of the line.

c Draw a circle with its centre at one end of the line.

d Draw a circle with its centre at the other end of the line. The circles should have the same radius.

e Draw a straight line to join the points where the circles cross.

7 Use your diagram from **Q6**.

    a Measure the angle between the 8 cm line and its bisector.

    b Measure the length of the bisector on each side of the 8 cm line.

    c Reasoning Explain why the bisector is a perpendicular bisector.

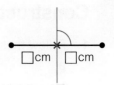

Constructing an angle bisector

> **Key point** A line that cuts an angle in half is called an **angle bisector**.
>
>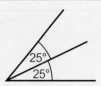

1 Which of these angles have a bisector?

    a   **b**    **c**    **d**

2 Follow these steps to bisect an angle.

    a    **b** 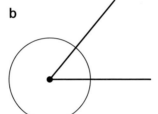   **c**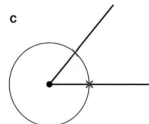

    d 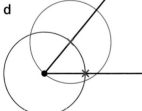   **e** 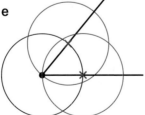   **f**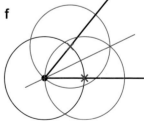

    a Draw an acute angle.

    b Draw a circle with its centre at the point of the angle.

    c Draw crosses where the circle cuts the arms of the angle.

    Keep your compasses open the same distance.

    d Put the compass point on one cross and draw a circle.

    e Put the compass point on the other cross and draw a circle.

    f Draw a straight line through the points where the circles cross.

Constructing a perpendicular from a point to a line

1 Follow these steps to draw a perpendicular to a line from a point above the line.

a

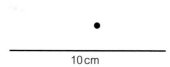

b

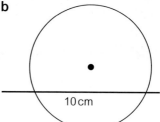

c

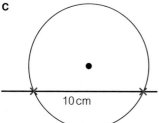

d

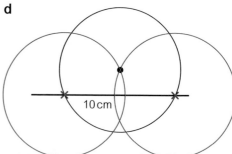

e

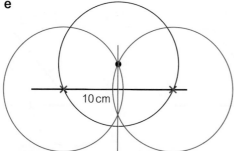

a Draw a straight line of length 10 cm. Draw a dot above the line.

b Put the compass point on the dot and draw a circle that crosses the line in two places. Keep your compasses open the same distance.

c Draw crosses where the circle cuts the line.

d Draw overlapping circles, with the same radius, with their centres on the crosses.

e Draw a straight line through the points where the circles cross. This should go through the dot.

Reflect Hakan starts writing tips for drawing a perpendicular bisector.

He writes:

– Use a sharp pencil.

– Make the circle radius longer than half the length of the line.

Write more tips to help you draw a perpendicular bisector. Do the same for an angle bisector.

5.3 Constructing triangles

- Construct accurate triangles
- Construct accurate nets of solids involving triangles

Constructing a triangle when you know the side lengths

Guided

1 Follow these steps to draw a triangle.

   a   **b**   **c**

 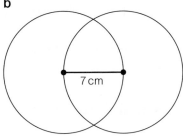 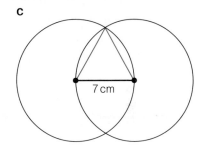

   7 cm   7 cm   7 cm

   a Draw a straight line of length 7 cm.

   b At each end of the line draw a circle with radius 7 cm.

   c Draw a straight line to join each end of the 7 cm line to one of the points where the circles cross.

   d Measure and label each side of the triangle.

   e **Reasoning**   What type of triangle have you drawn?

Guided

2 Follow these steps to draw a triangle.

   a   **b**   **c**   **d**

  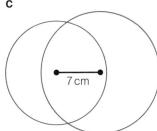 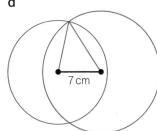

   7 cm   7 cm   7 cm   7 cm

   a Draw a straight line of length 7 cm.

   b Draw a circle with radius 8 cm with its centre at one end of the line.

   c Draw a circle with radius 9 cm with its centre at the other end of the line.

   d Draw a straight line to join each end of the 7 cm line to one of the points where the circles cross.

   e Measure and label each side of the triangle.

3 Follow these steps to draw a triangle.

a b 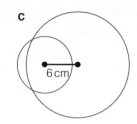 c d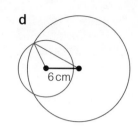

a Draw a straight line of length 6 cm.

b Draw a circle with radius 5 cm with its centre at one end of the line.

c Draw a circle with radius 9 cm with its centre at the other end of the line.

d Draw a straight line to join each end of the 6 cm line to one of the points where the circles cross.

e Write down what you think the side lengths of your triangle will be.

f Measure each side of the triangle to check your answers to part **e**.

Constructing a right-angled triangle

1 Follow these instructions to construct this right-angled triangle.

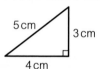

a
_____
8 cm

b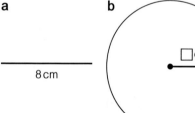

c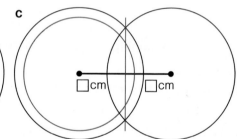

d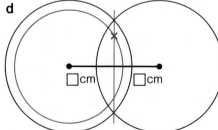

e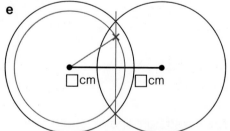

a Draw a line of length 8 cm.

b Construct the perpendicular bisector of your line.

> **Q1a hint** This line needs to be twice as long as the base of the triangle.

  i Draw a circle at each end of the line so that the two circles overlap. The circles should have the same radius.

  ii Draw a straight line through the points where the two circles cross.

c Construct the sloping side of the triangle.

  i Open your compasses to 5 cm.

  ii Draw a circle with its centre at the left-hand end of the line.

d Draw a cross where the circle crosses the vertical line.

e Draw the sloping line with a ruler between the centre dot and the cross.

Constructing a net of a solid

Guided

1 Follow these instructions to construct a net of this square-based pyramid on centimetre squared paper.

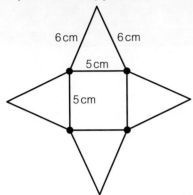

a

b

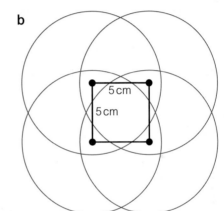

c

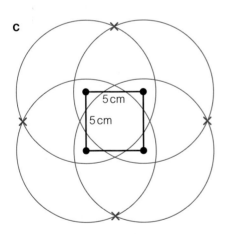

d

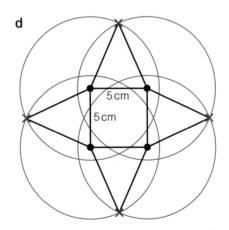

a Draw a square of side length 5 cm on centimetre squared paper. Draw a dot at each corner of the square.

b Draw 4 circles of radius 6 cm, each with their centre at a corner of the square.

c Draw a cross at the outer points where the circles meet.

d Join the crosses to the dots to create the triangular faces of the pyramid.

Reflect　　Write down the steps you would follow to construct a triangle with sides 6 cm, 8 cm and 11 cm. Compare your steps with a partner's.

5.4 Using accurate scale diagrams

- Construct and draw accurate scale diagrams
- Use scale diagrams to solve problems

Drawing a triangle accurately

1 Use a ruler and a protractor to draw these angles accurately.

a 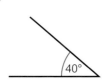   b 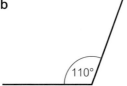   c   d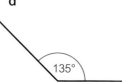

Guided

2 Follow these instructions to draw this triangle accurately.

a   b 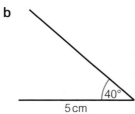   c 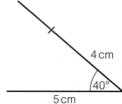   d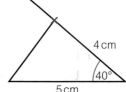

    a Draw a line of length 5 cm.

    b Measure an angle of 40° at the right-hand end of the line. Draw a long line.

    c Measure 4 cm along the line. Draw a cross to mark it.

    d Join the end of the 5 cm line to the cross to create a triangle.

Constructing a scale diagram

Guided

1 The diagram shows the cross-section of one side of a roof.
A builder wants an accurate drawing using a scale of 1 cm to 1 m.

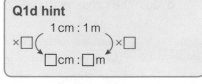

    a Work out the drawing measurement for each real-life distance.

      i 10 m   **ii** 4 m

> **Q1a hint** Copy the diagram. As you work out the drawing measurements, write them on your diagram.

    b Make an accurate scale drawing of the roof.

The builder wants to know the length x.

    c Measure x on your diagram in centimetres.

    d Work out the length in metres.

> **Q1d hint**
>
> $$\times\square \overset{1\,\text{cm}\,:\,1\,\text{m}}{\left(\right)} \times\square$$
>
> $\square\text{cm}:\square\text{m}$

2 The diagram shows a ladder leaning against a house.
The wall of the house meets the ground at a right angle.
A painter wants the ladder to touch the house 12 m above
the ground. For safety, the ladder should be inclined at
an angle of 75°.
Follow these steps to make an accurate scale drawing of the situation.
Use a scale of 1 cm to 2 m.

  a Work out the drawing measurement for 12 m.

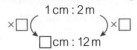

> **Q2a hint** Copy the diagram. As you work out the drawing measurement and the angle, write them on your diagram.

  b Work out the size of the third angle in the triangle.
  c Draw a vertical line to represent 12 m.

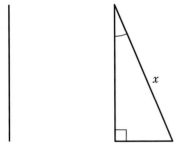

  d Use a protractor to draw
     i a 90° angle at the bottom of the line
     ii the angle you found in part **b** at the top of the line.
  e Measure length x on your diagram.
  f Use the scale to work out the real-life length.

> **Q2f hint**
>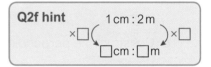

Distance from a point to a line

1 For each diagram
   i measure the length of line 1 in centimetres
   ii measure the length of line 2 in centimetres
   iii state which line is shorter.

a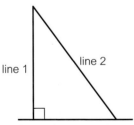

b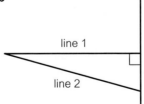

c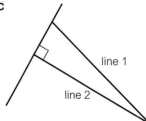

  d Reasoning What do the three shorter lines have in common?

2 **Problem-solving** The sketched plan shows
three towns, A, B and C.
A new road is to be built to join town A to
the road between towns B and C.
Follow these steps to make an accurate drawing of the plan.
Use a scale of 1 cm to 4 km.

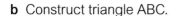

> **Q2a hint** Copy the diagram. As you
> work out the drawing measurements,
> write them on your diagram.

a Work out the drawing measurements for the
three sides of the triangle.

   i AB   **ii** BC   **iii** AC

b Construct triangle ABC.

   i Draw side BC.

   ii Use compasses to draw two circles and join the point where they cross to B and C to
make a triangle.

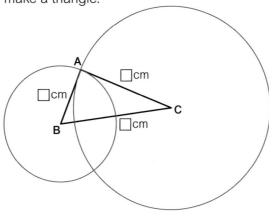

c Construct the perpendicular from A to the line BC.

i   **ii**   **iii**

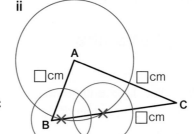 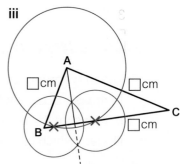

   i Draw a circle around point A that crosses the line BC. Mark two crosses where the
circle cuts the line.

   ii Draw overlapping circles, with the same radius, around the crosses.

   iii Draw a straight line through where the circles cross to point A.

d Measure the length of the road on your diagram.

e Work out the length of the road in kilometres.

> **Q2e hint**
>
>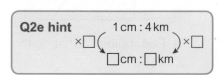

Reflect   Architects use scale diagrams when they design buildings. What are the
advantages of using a scale diagram? Who else might use a scale diagram? Discuss your
answers with a partner.

6 Sequences, inequalities, equations and proportion

6.1 nth term of arithmetic sequences

- Use the nth term to generate an arithmetic sequence
- Find and use the nth term of an arithmetic sequence

Using the nth term

1 Copy and complete the table for each sequence, showing the **term** and its **position**. Each table has been started for you.

a 10, 20, 30, 40, 50, ...

Position (n)	1	2	3	4	5
Term ($10n$)	10	20	30	☐	☐

b 4, 5, 6, 7, 8, ...

Position (n)	1	2	3	4	5
Term ($n + 3$)	4	5	☐	☐	8

c 3, 5, 7, 9, ...

Position (n)	1	2	3	4	5
Term ($2n + 1$)	3	☐	☐	☐	☐

d 5, 8, 11, ...

Position (n)	1	2	3	4	5
Term ($3n + 2$)	☐	☐	☐	☐	☐

2 Copy and complete the tables to work out the first five terms of each sequence.

a nth term = $2n$

Position (n)	1	2	3	4	5
Term ($2n$)	$2 \times 1 = 2$	$2 \times 2 = 4$	$2 \times 3 =$ ☐	$2 \times$ ☐ $=$ ☐	☐ $\times$ ☐ $=$ ☐

b nth term = $n + 5$

Position (n)	1	2	3	4	5
Term ($n + 5$)	$1 + 5 = 6$	$2 + 5 =$ ☐	$3 +$ ☐ $=$ ☐	☐ $+$ ☐ $=$ ☐	

c nth term = $2n + 3$

Position (n)	1	2	3	4	5
Term ($2n + 3$)	$2 \times 1 + 3 = 5$	$2 \times 2 + 3 =$ ☐	$2 \times 3 +$ ☐ $=$ ☐	$2 \times$ ☐ $+$ ☐ $=$ ☐	

3 Work out the 3rd term of the sequence with nth term

    a $4n$ 3rd term is when $n = 3$ so 3rd term is $4 \times 3 = \square$

    b $n + 4$ **c** $3n + 1$ **d** $8n - 3$

> **Q3c hint** Remember the priority of operations: multiply then add.

4 Work out the 6th term and the 10th term of the sequence with nth term

    a $n - 5$ **b** $4n + 1$ **c** $8n - 3$

> **Q4 hint** For the 6th term, substitute $n = 6$ and for the 10th term substitute $n = 10$.

5 Work out the 2nd term of the sequence with nth term

    a $n - 9$ **b** $2n - 5$ **c** $3n - 9$

6 Copy and complete to find the first five terms of the sequence with nth term $7n - 4$.

    1st term is when $n = 1$ $7n - 4 = 7 \times 1 - 4 = \square$

    2nd term is when $n = 2$ $7n - 4 = 7 \times 2 - 4 = \square$

    3rd term is when $n = \square$ $7n - 4 = 7 \times \square - 4 = \square$

    4th term is when $n = \square$ $7n - 4 = \square \times \square - \square = \square$

    5th term is when $n = \square$ $7n - 4 =$

    First five terms are $\square, \square, \square, \square, \square$

7 Work out the 2nd term of the sequence with nth term

    a $-3n$ **b** $-4n + 7$ **c** $-7n - 2$

> **Q7 hint** A negative number multiplied by a positive number gives a negative number.

8 Work out the first five terms of each sequence.

    a $n + 7$ **b** $4n$ **c** $5n - 1$

9 Match the nth term on the top row of cards with the first five terms of its sequence on the bottom row of cards.

> **Q9 hint** Substitute $n = 1$, $n = 2$, $n = 3$, $n = 4$ and $n = 5$ into each nth term.

$5n$	$n + 5$	$3n + 1$	$n + 3$	$3n - 1$
4, 7, 10, 13, 16	2, 5, 8, 11, 14	5, 10, 15, 20, 25	4, 5, 6, 7, 8	6, 7, 8, 9, 10

Finding the nth term

1 **Problem-solving** Here are some sequences and their nth terms.

    i 3, 6, 9, 12, 15, ... nth term $= 3n$

    ii 5, 10, 15, 20, 25, ... nth term $= 5n$

    iii 7, 14, 21, 28, 35, ... nth term $= 7n$

    a For each sequence, find the **term-to-term rule**.

    b What pattern do you notice between the term-to-term rule and the nth term?

    c Write down what you think the nth term will be for this sequence: 2, 4, 6, 8, 10, ...

2 Match each nth term on the left with its sequence on the right. Use **Q1** to help you.

   a $10n$

   b $4n$

   c $11n$

   i 4, 8, 12, 16, 20, ...

   ii 11, 22, 33, 44, 55, ...

   iii 10, 20, 30, 40, 50, ...

3 All these sequences have term-to-term rule 'add 3'.

Work out the nth term of each sequence by comparing it with the sequence $3n$.
The first one has been started for you.

   a 5, 8, 11, 14, 17, ...

$3n$

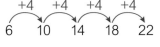

nth term is $3n + \square$

   b 1, 4, 7, 10, 13, ...   **c** 2, 5, 8, 11, 14, ...

4 Use the term-to-term rule to find the nth term. The first one has been started for you.

   a 6, 10, 14, 18, 22, ...

        +4 +4 +4 +4
        6 10 14 18 22   Term-to-term rule is +4

Position (n)	1	2	3	4	5

$4n$

$4n + 2$

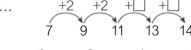

nth term is $4n + \square$

   b 7, 9, 11, 13, 15, ...

        +2 +2 +$\square$ +$\square$
        7 9 11 13 14   Term-to-term rule is +$\square$

Position (n)	1	2	3	4	5

$2n$

$2n + \square$

nth term is $\square n + \square$

   c 4, 7, 10, 13, 16, ...

        +$\square$ +$\square$ +$\square$ +$\square$
        4 7 10 13 16   Term-to-term rule is +$\square$

Position (n)	1	2	3	4	5

$\square n$

$\square n + \square$

nth term is $\square n + \square$

   d 1, 6, 11, 16, 21, ...

        +$\square$ +$\square$ +$\square$ +$\square$
        1 6 11 16 21   Term-to-term rule is +$\square$

Position (n)	1	2	3	4	5

$\square n$

$\square n - \square$

nth term is $\square n - \square$

   e 13, 16, 19, 22, 25, ... nth term is $\square n + \square$

5 For each sequence
   i work out the nth term
   ii work out the 10th term using the nth term from part **i**.
   a 6, 9, 12, 15, 18, ...
   b 2, 7, 12, 17, 22, ...
   c 15, 17, 19, 21, 23, ...

6 State the nth term for each descending sequence.
   Some parts have been started for you.
   a 10, 8, 6, 4, 2, ... nth term: $-2n + \square$
   b 14, 11, 8, 5, 2, ... nth term: $-\square n + 17$
   c 20, 19, 18, 17, 16, ... nth term: $-\square n + \square$
   d $-3, -6, -9, -12, -15, ...$ nth term: $-\square n$
   e $-4, -8, -12, -16, -20, ...$ nth term: $-\square n$

Q6 hint In a descending sequence, each term is less than the term before it.

Q6a hint When $n = 1$, $10 = -2n + \square$

7 For the sequence $-7, -11, -15, -19, -23$, find
   a the nth term
   b the 20th term.

8 **Problem-solving** Katie puts out chairs for assembly.
   She puts 3 in the first row, 5 in the second row, 7 in the third row and so on.

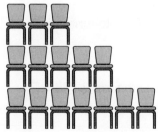

   Find
   a the nth term describing the sequence of the numbers of chairs she puts out
   b the number of chairs in the 10th row.

9 **Problem-solving** Chris has a bag of sweets.
   The number of sweets he eats each day is given by the nth term $3n - 1$.
   Find
   a the number of sweets he eats on days 1, 2 and 3
   b the number of sweets he eats in total in the first 3 days.

Reflect   Carla starts to write the steps for finding the nth term of a sequence.
'1   Work out the term-to-term rule.'
Write your own list of steps for finding the nth term of a sequence.

6.2 Non-linear sequences

- Recognise and continue geometric sequences
- Recognise and continue quadratic sequences

Geometric sequences

1 For each geometric sequence
 i write down the term-to-term rule
 ii write down the 4th term.
 The first one has been started for you.

a 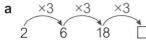 term-to-term rule: ×3

b 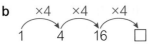 term-to-term rule: ×□

c 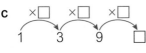 term-to-term rule: ×□

d 2   20   200   □   term-to-term rule: ×□

2 Use the term-to-term rule to continue these geometric sequences.

a Term-to-term rule: ×10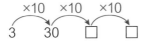

b Term-to-term rule: ×2

c Term-to-term rule: ×3

3 Work out the related division to find the missing number in each multiplication.
 a $2 \times \square = 5$ Related division: $5 \div 2 = \square$
 b $3 \times \square = 4.5$ Related division: $\square \div \square = \square$
 c $4 \times \square = 2$ Related division: $\square \div \square = \square$
 d $8 \times \square = 12$ Related division: $\square \div \square = \square$

4 All of these are geometric sequences.
 For each one, write the term-to-term rule and find the next two terms.
 The first one has been started for you.
 a 2, 3, □, □, ...   2nd term ÷ 1st term = 3 ÷ 2 = □   term-to-term rule: ×1.5
 b 48, 24, □, □, ...   2nd term ÷ 1st term = □ ÷ □ = □   term-to-term rule: × □
 c 20, 8, □, □, ...   2nd term ÷ 1st term = □ ÷ □ = □   term-to-term rule: × □

	Term-to-term rule	Examples
Arithmetic sequence	Add or subtract same number each time	$\overset{+4}{\frown}\ \overset{+4}{\frown}\ \overset{+4}{\frown}\ \overset{+4}{\frown}$ 5,　9,　13,　17,　… $\overset{-2}{\frown}\ \overset{-2}{\frown}\ \overset{-2}{\frown}\ \overset{-2}{\frown}$ 17,　15,　13,　11,　…
Geometric sequence	Multiply by same number each time	$\overset{\times2}{\frown}\ \overset{\times2}{\frown}\ \overset{\times2}{\frown}\ \overset{\times2}{\frown}$ 6,　12,　24,　48,　… $\overset{\times0.1}{\frown}\ \overset{\times0.1}{\frown}\ \overset{\times0.1}{\frown}\ \overset{\times0.1}{\frown}$ 500,　50,　5,　0.5,　…

5　**Reasoning**　For each sequence, write A or G to show if it is arithmetic or geometric.
　　a i　2, 4, 8, 16, 32, …　　　**b i**　5, 25, 45, 65, …　　　**c i**　10, 5, 0, −5, …
　　ii　2, 4, 6, 8, 10, 12, …　　　**ii**　5, 25, 125, 625, …　　　**ii**　10, 5, 2.5, 1.25, …

6　**Reasoning**　Decide whether or not each sequence is geometric.
　　a 4, 20, 100, 500, …　**b** 12, 14, 16, 18, …　**c** 2, 4, 12, 48, …

> **Q6 hint** Do you multiply by the same number to get from term to term in the sequence?

7　**Problem-solving**　Chen puts £1 into a savings jar in the first week, £2 in the second week, £4 in the third week and so on. The amounts she puts into the savings jar form a geometric sequence.
　　a What is the term-to-term rule of the sequence?
　　b How much does she put in the jar in the fourth week?
　　c How much is in the savings jar in total after five weeks?

Quadratic sequences

1　The diagram shows the first three terms in a pattern sequence.

　　a Draw the next pattern in the sequence.
　　　Write the number of squares underneath.
　　b What is the name for the numbers in the sequence?
　　c Write the next four terms in the sequence.
　　Hilary works out the differences between terms like this.

　　d Copy and continue the pattern to work out the differences between terms.

Key point A **quadratic sequence** has an nth term that includes n^2 (and no higher power of n).

2 Here is the **quadratic sequence** with nth term $n^2 + 2$.

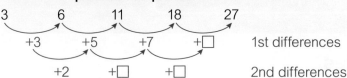

a Find the missing 1st difference.
b What is the pattern in the 1st differences?
c Find the missing 2nd difference.
d Use the pattern of differences to find the next term in the sequence.

3 Here is a quadratic sequence.

8, 9, 11, 14, 18, ...

a Work out the 1st and 2nd differences.
b Work out the 6th and 7th terms.

4 Copy and complete to find the first five terms of the quadratic sequence with nth term $3n^2$.
For $n = 1$, $3n^2 = 3 \times 1^2 = 3 \times 1 = \square$
For $n = 2$, $3n^2 = 3 \times 2^2 = 3 \times \square = \square$
For $n = 3$, $3n^2 = 3 \times \square^2 = 3 \times \square = \square$
For $n = 4$, $3n^2 =$
For $n = 5$,
First five terms are $\square$, $\square$, $\square$, $\square$, $\square$

5 Write down the first five terms of the quadratic sequences with nth term
a $2n^2$
b $n^2 + 1$
c $3n^2 + 2$

6 **Problem-solving** Which has the larger 5th term, the geometric sequence 2, 6, 18, ... or the quadratic sequence with nth term $4n^2$?

Q6 hint Write out the first five terms of each sequence.

Reflect For each of the types of sequence given below
a in your own words, describe what the term-to-term rule is
b write an example.
i arithmetic sequence   **ii** geometric sequence   **iii** quadratic sequence

6.3 Inequalities

- Represent inequalities on a number line
- Find integer values that satisfy an inequality

Interpreting inequalities

1 For each **inequality**, copy and complete by circling all the integers that **satisfy** x. The first one has been done for you.

> **Q1 hint Satisfies** means 'makes a statement true'. What does $x \geqslant 6$ mean in words?

   a $x \geqslant 6$ $x = 1$ $x = 4$ $\boxed{x = 6}$ $\boxed{x = 9}$

   b $x < 3$ $x = 2$ $x = 3$ $x = 4$ $x = 7$

   c $x > 4$ $x = 2$ $x = 3$ $x = 4$ $x = 6$

   d $x \leqslant 4$ $x = 0$ $x = 2$ $x = 4$ $x = 9$

2 For each inequality, write down an integer that satisfies x.

   a $x \leqslant 6$ **b** $x > 2$ **c** $x \geqslant 5$ **d** $x < 7$

> **Q2a hint** This means x is less than or equal to 6. So, x can be $\square$.

Showing inequalities on number lines

1 Match each inequality on the cards in the top row with the correct number line on a card in the bottom row.

> **Q1 hint** A filled circle shows that the value is included. An empty circle shows that the value is not included.

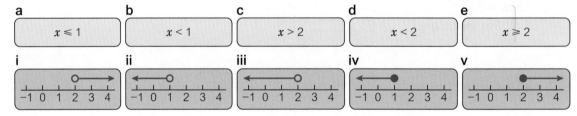

2 Show each inequality on a number line. The first one has been done for you.

   a $x \leqslant 3$

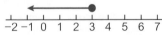

   b $x \geqslant 5$ **c** $x > 2$ **d** $x < 3$

> **Q2b hint** Start by drawing a circle above 5 on the number line.

3 Write the inequality shown by each number line.

   a 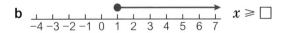 $x > \square$

   b $x \geqslant \square$

   c $x > \square$

   d $x \ldots \square$

Key point 1 < x < 3 is a two-sided inequality.

x can take values between 1 and 3.

x does not equal 1 or 3.

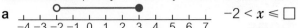

4 Write the inequality shown by each number line. Some have been started for you.

a 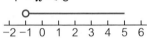 −2 < x ⩽ □

b □ ⩽ x ⩽ 4

c □ ... x ... □

d □ ... x ... □

5 Show each inequality on a number line. The first one has been started for you.

a −1 < x ⩽ 5

b 1 < x < 5　　　**c** 0 ⩽ x < 2　　　**d** −2 ⩽ x ⩽ 3

6 Match each two-sided inequality on the cards in the top row with the correct number line on the cards on the bottom row.

a −1 ⩽ x ⩽ 2　　**b** −1 < x < 2　　**c** −1 < x ⩽ 2　　**d** −1 ⩽ x < 2

i 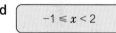　　**ii**　　**iii**　　**iv**

7 Write down the integer values that satisfy each inequality.

a −2 < x ⩽ 4

b −3 ⩽ x < 3

c 1 ⩽ x ⩽ 3

d 0 < x < 5

Q7a hint Draw a number line and circle the whole numbers.

−2 < x ⩽ 4

8 **Problem-solving** Geraint says his age is more than 7 but less than or equal to 14.

a Show his age using a number line.

b Write Geraint's age as an inequality.

c Write down all the possible ages he could be (to the nearest year).

9 **Problem-solving** Mira says that the ages of her siblings can be shown as 10 ⩽ x ⩽ 17. In two years' time, what will the inequality be?

Reflect Write down any new words, symbols or representations that you have learned in this lesson and what they mean. Compare your list with a partner's list.

6.4 Solving equations

- Construct and solve equations including fractions or powers

Solving equations with fractions

> **Key point** You can write a fraction as a division.
>
> For example, $\frac{1}{2} = 1 \div 2$ and $\frac{x+1}{2} = (x+1) \div 2$

1 Rewrite each equation with brackets and a division sign.

   a $\dfrac{x+2}{7} = 4$ **b** $\dfrac{x-1}{8} = 6$ **c** $1 = \dfrac{x-12}{4}$

Guided

2 Write each equation as a function machine. The first one has been started for you.

   a $\dfrac{x-3}{15} = 1$ $(x-3) \div 15 = 1$

   $x \rightarrow \boxed{}) \rightarrow \boxed{}) \rightarrow \square$

   > **Q2 hint** Use **Q1** to help.

   b $\dfrac{a+2}{3} = 2$

   c $\dfrac{y+7}{4} = 9$

   d $\dfrac{d-10}{2} = 20$

> **Worked example**
>
> Use a function machine to solve the equation $\dfrac{c+6}{5} = 2$.
>
> $\dfrac{c+6}{5} = 2$
>
> $(c+6) \div 5 = 2$ — Rewrite the fraction as a division.
>
> $c \rightarrow \boxed{+6} \rightarrow \boxed{\div 5} \rightarrow 2$
> $4 \leftarrow \boxed{-6} \leftarrow \boxed{\times 5} \leftarrow 2$
>
> Write each operation as a step in a function machine.
> Then work backwards, using inverse operations, to work out the value of c.
>
> $c = 4$
>
> Check: $\dfrac{c+6}{5} = \dfrac{4+6}{5} = \dfrac{10}{5} = 2$ ✓ — Check your answer by substituting your value back into the equation.

3 Use a function machine to solve each equation.

   a $\dfrac{x-1}{2} = 5$

   b $\dfrac{y+1}{4} = 2$

   c $\dfrac{x+5}{7} = 3$

   > **Q3 hint** Remember to check your answers.

Use the balancing method to solve the equation $\frac{a-2}{6} = 3$.

$\frac{a-2}{6} = 3$

$(a-2) \div 6 = 3$ — Rewrite the fraction as a division.

$(a-2) \div 6 = 3$

$\times 6 \big(\qquad \big) \times 6$

$a - 2 = 18$ — $\times 6$ on both sides

$+2 \big(\qquad \big) +2$ — $+2$ on both sides

$a = 20$

Check: $\frac{a-2}{6} = \frac{20-2}{6} = \frac{18}{6} = 3$ ✓

4   Use the balancing method to solve each equation.

Q4 hint Remember to check your answers. You can use a function machine to check too.

a $\frac{a+8}{10} = 4$ 　　　　**b** $\frac{b-7}{5} = 6$

c $\frac{c+10}{2} = 14$ 　　　**d** $\frac{d+1}{3} = 8$

e $\frac{e-9}{9} = 1$ 　　　　**f** $\frac{f-12}{3} = -3$

5   **Problem-solving**   Kelly thinks of a number n. She then subtracts 3 and divides by 4.

a Copy and complete the expression: $\frac{n - \square}{\square}$

Kelly's answer is 7.

b Copy and complete the equation: $\frac{n - \square}{\square} = \square$

c Solve the equation to work out the value of n.

Solving equations with powers

The inverse operation of squaring is taking the square root.
For example, $3^2 = 9$ and $\sqrt{9} = 3$.
When taking the square root of a number, there is a **positive** and a **negative** solution.
For example, if $x^2 = 4$, then $x = \pm\sqrt{4}$ so $x = +2$ or $x = -2$.

1   Solve these equations. Give the positive **and** negative solutions each time.
The first one has been done for you.

a $x^2 = 25$
　　$x = \pm\sqrt{25}$
　　$x = +5$ or $x = -5$

b $x^2 = 9$

c $x^2 = 100$

d $x^2 = 64$

e $x^2 = 36$

2 Solve these equations. Give the positive **and** negative solutions each time.
The first one has been started for you.

a $x^2 + 7 = 23$

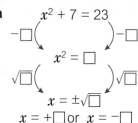

$x^2 = \square$

$x = \pm\sqrt{\square}$

$x = +\square$ or $x = -\square$

> **Q2a hint** Check your solutions
> $(\square)^2 + 7 = \square$ and $(-\square)^2 + 7 = \square$

b $x^2 - 5 = 20$

c $x^2 + 4 = 40$

d $a^2 + 7 = 107$

e $e^2 + 2 = 66$

f $1 + b^2 = 10$

> **Q2f hint** $1 + b^2$ is
> the same as $b^2 + 1$

3 For each equation, find the positive solution correct to 1 decimal place.
The first one has been started for you.

a $x^2 - 3 = 10$

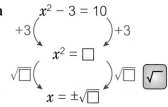

$x^2 = \square$

$x = \pm\sqrt{\square}$

Only the positive solution is required.

$x = \square$ to 1 d.p.

$\boxed{3.6055512?}$

b $x^2 - 4 = 19$

c $x^2 + 3 = 11$

4 A square sticky note has side length x cm.
a Write an expression for the area in terms of x.
The area is $49\,\text{cm}^2$.
b Write an equation for the area.
c **Problem-solving** Solve the equation to work out the side length of the sticky note.
d **Reasoning** Why is there only a positive solution for this problem?

> **Reflect**   Which operations did you use in this lesson? Write down the inverse of each of
> the operations you used.

6.5 Proportion

- Write formulae connecting variables in direct or inverse proportion
- Use algebra to solve problems involving direct or inverse proportion

Writing formulae for direct proportion

1 **a** Work out the gradient of the line.

Q1a hint For every 1 square right, how many squares up does the line go?

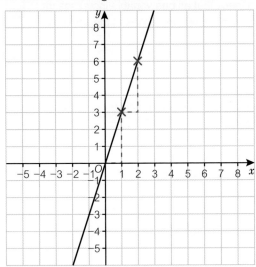

b Write down its y-intercept.

c Write the equation of the line.

Q1c hint Use parts **a** and **b** to help you. $y = \square x + \square$

> **Key point** When two variables x and y are in **direct proportion**, they can be represented by the formula $y = kx$, where k is a constant value.
> As one variable increases, the other variable increases **at the same rate**.

Guided

2 Does each data set show direct proportion?
The first one has been started for you.

a

$\times 2 \quad \times 2 \quad \times 2$

x	1	2	4	8
y	3	6	12	24

$\times 2 \quad \times 2 \quad \times 2$

b

x	1	2	4	8
y	2	3	4	5

c

x	3	9	27	81
y	2	6	18	54

Worked example

Olivia measures how far she has walked at different times.

Time, t (h)	0.5	1	1.5	2
Distance, d (km)	3	6	9	12

a Show that t and d are in direct proportion.

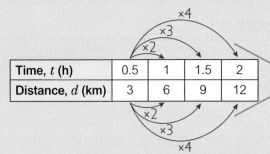

Check that as one variable increases the other variable increases at the same rate.

When time t doubles, so does distance d. When time t is multiplied by 3, so is distance d. Therefore, t and d are in direct proportion.

b Write the formula connecting t and d.

$d = kt$ ——— Write a statement like $y = kx$ but using the letters t and d instead of x and y.

Use $d = 6$ and $t = 1$ ——— You can choose and substitute any values for d and t from the table. Choose easy numbers to work with.

$6 = k \times 1$ ——— Solve to find k.

$k = 6$

Formula is $d = 6t$ ——— Substitute k back into the formula.

Check: $d = 12$ and $t = 2$

$12 = 6 \times 2$ ✓ ——— Check your formula by substituting other values for d and t.

c Use your formula to calculate how far Olivia will walk in 3 hours.

$d = 6 \times 3 = 18\,\text{km}$ ——— Substitute $t = 3$ into $d = 6t$.

In 3 hours she will walk 18 km.

Guided

3 Changsu measures the distance a turtle travels at different times.

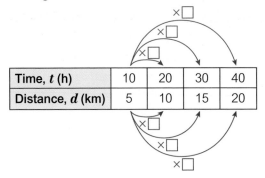

Time, t (h)	10	20	30	40
Distance, d (km)	5	10	15	20

a Show that t and d are in direct proportion.

b Write a formula using d, t and k.

c Write the formula connecting d and t.

d Using your formula from part **c**, calculate how far the turtle will travel in 1 hour.

Q3c hint Solve to find the value of k.

4 In a science experiment, students measure how far a spring extends when different masses are hung from it. The results are shown in this graph.

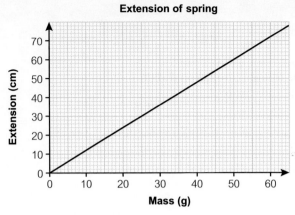

Extension of spring

a Copy and complete the table, using the graph.

Mass (g)		25		50
Extension (cm)	20		40	

b Are extension and mass in direct proportion?

c Write a formula connecting mass, m, and extension, e.

> **Q4b hint** Use your answer to part **a** to help you.

> **Q4c hint** Write a statement like $y = kx$ but use the letters in the problem.

5 Maida buys 5 bananas for 70p. The cost of bananas, c, is in direct proportion to the number of bananas, n.

a How much will 10 bananas cost?

b Write a formula for the cost, in pence, of n bananas.

c Using the formula from part **b**, find the cost of 30 bananas.

6 x and y are in direct proportion to each other.
When x is 20, y is 200.

a Write the formula connecting x and y.

b Using the formula from part **a**, work out the value of y when x is 7.

Writing formulae for inverse proportion

> **Key point**   When two quantities are in **inverse proportion**, as one increases the other decreases **at the same rate**. They can be represented by the formula $y = \dfrac{k}{x}$.

1 Does each data set show inverse proportion? The first one has been started for you.

a

×2   ×2   ×2

x	1	2	4	8
y	40	20	10	5

÷2   ÷2   ÷2

b

x	1	2	4	8
y	11	9	7	5

c

x	1	3	9	27
y	18	6	2	$\frac{2}{3}$

Worked example

It takes 2 people 2 hours to paint a room.

a How long does it take 4 people?

Number of people : Time (hours)

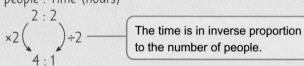

The time is in inverse proportion to the number of people.

b Find the formula connecting the amount of time, t, and the number of people, n.

$$n = \frac{k}{t}$$ ── This is the formula for inverse proportion.

Use $n = 2$ and $t = 2$

$$2 = \frac{k}{2}$$ ── Solve to find k.

$$k = 4$$

Formula is $n = \frac{4}{t}$

c Use your formula to calculate how many people are needed to paint the room in half an hour.

$$n = \frac{4}{0.5} = 8$$ ── Substitute $t = 0.5$ into the formula.

8 people are needed.

2 It takes 2 people 1 day to build a garden.

  a How long does it take 1 person?

  b Find the formula connecting the amount of time, t, and the number of people, n.

  c Use your formula to work out how many people are needed to build the garden in half a day.

3 **Problem-solving** x and y are in inverse proportion to each other.
When $x = 4$, $y = 3$.

  a Work out the formula connecting x and y.

  b Use your formula to work out the value of y when x is 6.

> **Q3a hint** Substitute x and y into $y = \frac{k}{x}$ to find k.

Reflect   Look at this set of data.

x	2	4	6	8
y	1	2	4	7

Tim says that both sets of values are increasing, so they are in direct proportion.
He is wrong. Explain why.

7 Circles, Pythagoras and prisms

7.1 Circumference of a circle

- Calculate the circumference of a circle
- Estimate calculations involving pi (π)
- Solve problems involving the circumference of a circle

Parts of a circle

1 **a** Draw a circle with a pair of compasses.

b Mark the centre of the circle with a dot. Label it O.

c Label the circumference.

d Use a ruler to draw a straight line from the centre O to the circumference of the circle. Label this line 'radius'.

e Use a ruler to draw a straight line through the centre O, touching the circumference of the circle at both ends. Label this line 'diameter'.

> **Q1c hint** The perimeter of a circle is called the circumference.

> **Q1d hint**
>

> **Q1e hint**
>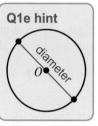

2 **Reasoning** Look at your diagram in **Q1**. Decide whether each statement is true or false.

a The diameter is twice the length of the radius.

b The diameter is $\frac{1}{2}$ the length of the radius.

c The diameter is longer than the radius.

d The circumference is longer than the diameter.

e Diameter = 2 × radius

3 Copy and complete the calculations. The first one has been started for you.

a
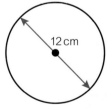
12 cm
Diameter = 12 cm
Radius = $\frac{1}{2}$ of □ = □ cm

b
22 cm
Diameter = □ cm
Radius = □ of □ = □ cm

c
9 cm
Radius = □ cm
Diameter = 2 × □ = □ cm

d
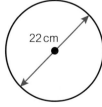
7 cm
Radius = □ cm
Diameter = □ × □ = □ cm

Guided

Calculating the circumference of a circle

1 π is a Greek letter called pi.

   a Find π on a key on your calculator. Press it. Write down the value of π to 2 decimal places.

   b Use your calculator to work out to 1 decimal place

     i 2π   **ii** 3π   **iii** π × 4   **iv** π × 5   **Q1bi hint** 2π = 2 × π

2 The formula to find the circumference of a circle of any diameter is

      circumference = π × diameter   or $C = \pi d$

   Use this formula to work out the circumference of each circle.

   Give your answers to 1 decimal place.

a
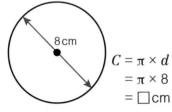

b
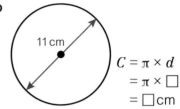

c
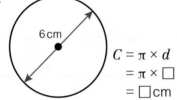

d
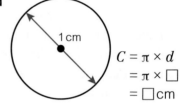

3 **Reasoning** Aisha and Olivia are calculating the circumference of a circle.

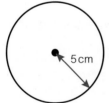

Aisha writes

Diameter   = 2 × 5 = 10 cm

Circumference = π × 10

              = 31.4 cm

Olivia writes

Circumference = 2 × π × r

              = 2 × π × 5

              = 31.4 cm

Explain why both of their calculations are correct.

4 **Problem-solving** A circular cake has diameter 20 cm.

   Tom is buying a ribbon to put around the outside of the cake.

   a Work out the circumference of the cake. Round your answer to the nearest cm.

   Tom needs an extra 5 cm overlap to stick the ends of the ribbon together.

   b What length of ribbon does Tom need?

   The ribbon is sold in lengths of 10 cm.

   c What length of ribbon should Tom buy?

   The ribbon costs 20p per 10 cm.

   d How much does it cost Tom to buy the ribbon?

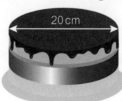

Q4c hint Do you need to round up or down to the nearest 10 cm?

Reflect Write down any new words you have learned in this lesson. Make sure you spell them correctly. Beside each one, write down its definition.

7.2 Area of a circle

- Calculate the area of a circle
- Solve problems involving the area of a circle

Area of a circle

Worked example

Calculate the area of a circle with radius 10 cm. Round your answer to 1 decimal place.

Area of a circle = πr^2 — | This is the formula for the area of a circle. |

$= \pi \times 10^2$ — | Follow the priority of operations and work out 10^2 first. |

$= \pi \times 100$

$= 314.159265...$

$= 314.2 \text{ cm}^2$ — | Round your answer to 1 d.p. as instructed in the question. |

1 Work out the area of each circle. Round your answers to 1 decimal place.

a

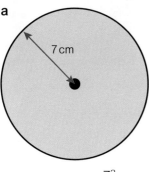

7 cm

area $= \pi \times 7^2$

$= \pi \times \square$

$= \square \text{ cm}^2$

b

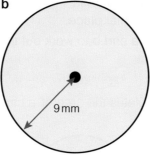

9 mm

area $= \pi \times \square^2$

$= \square \times \square$

$= \square \text{ mm}^2$

c

1 m

area $= \pi \times \square^{\square}$

$= \square \times \square$

$= \square \text{ m}^2$

d

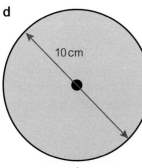

10 cm

radius $= \frac{1}{2}$ of $10 = \square$

area $= \pi \times 5^2$

$= \pi \times \square$

$= \square \text{ cm}^2$

e

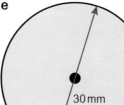

30 mm

radius $= \frac{1}{2}$ of $\square = \square$

area $= \pi \times \square$

$= \square \times \square$

$= \square \text{ mm}^2$

f

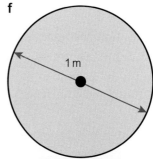

1 m

radius $= \frac{1}{2}$ of $\square = \square$

area $= \pi \times \square$

$= \square \times \square$

$= \square \text{ m}^2$

| **Q1d–f hint** You need to use the radius to calculate area. To find the radius **halve** the diameter. |

Guided

2 Sophia is working out the area of a circular lawn.
She finds the approximate area by using $\pi \approx 3$.
Here is her working.

area $= \pi \times 4^2$
$\approx 3 \times 4^2$
$= 3 \times 16$
$= 48\,m^2$

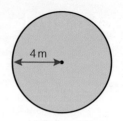

a Use Sophia's method to work out the approximate area of a circular lawn with radius 2 m.

b Calculate the exact area of the lawn.
Round your answer to 1 decimal place.

c **Reasoning**   Is your approximation larger or smaller than the exact area? Explain why.

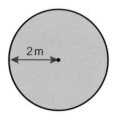

Solving problems involving the area of a circle

1 A photo frame is made from a square piece of wood, 15 cm by 15 cm.
A circular hole, with radius 5 cm, is cut out of the wood.

a Calculate the area of the square piece of wood.

b Calculate the area of the circular hole.
Round your answer to 1 decimal place.

c Use your answers to parts **a** and **b** to work out the area of the wooden photo frame.

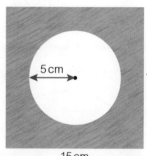

2 **Problem-solving**   Matt calculates the area of a circle with radius 12 cm.
Here is his working.

area $= \pi \times r^2$
$= \pi \times 12^2$
$= 452.4\,cm^2$ to 1 d.p.

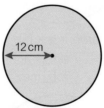

Use Matt's answer to work out the area of

a

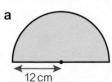

12 cm

b

12 cm

> **Q2 hint** What fraction of the whole circle is each shape?

> **Reflect**   How can you use an approximation of π to check that your answers to circle questions are sensible?

7.3 Pythagoras' theorem

- Find the length of an unknown side of a right-angled triangle
- Solve problems involving right-angled triangles

Calculating the length of the hypotenuse in a right-angled triangle

1 Identify the hypotenuse in each triangle.

a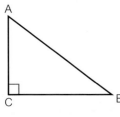

b

c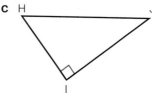

> **Q1a hint** The longest side of a right-angled triangle is called the **hypotenuse**. It is the side opposite the right angle.

2 Follow these steps to calculate the length of the hypotenuse.

  a Copy the triangle and label the hypotenuse c.

  b Label the other sides a and b.

  c Copy and complete. First write Pythagoras' theorem and then substitute the values of a and b.

> **Q2a hint** It doesn't matter which side you choose for a and which side you choose for b.

$$c^2 = a^2 + b^2$$
$$= \square^2 + \square^2$$
$$= \square + \square$$
$$= \square$$
$$c = \sqrt{\square}$$
$$= \square$$

3 Copy and complete to find the length of the hypotenuse in each right-angled triangle.

a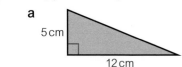

$$c^2 = 5^2 + 12^2$$
$$= 25 + \square$$
$$= \square$$
$$c = \sqrt{\square}$$
$$= \square$$

b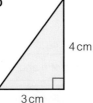

$$c^2 = 4^2 + \square^2$$
$$= \square + \square$$
$$= \square$$
$$c = \sqrt{\square}$$
$$= \square$$

c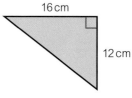

$$c^2 = \square^2 + \square^2$$
$$= \square + \square$$
$$= \square$$
$$c = \sqrt{\square}$$
$$= \square$$

4 Problem-solving A zip wire runs from the top of a vertical 10 m tree to the ground. The end of the zip wire is 24 m horizontally from the base of the tree. How long is the zip wire?

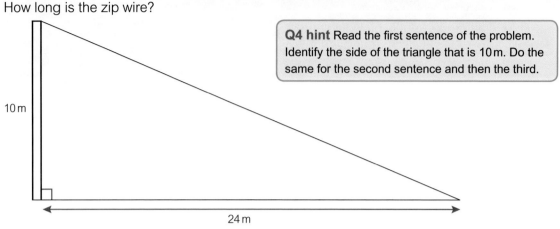

Q4 hint Read the first sentence of the problem. Identify the side of the triangle that is 10 m. Do the same for the second sentence and then the third.

10 m

24 m

Calculating the length of a shorter side in a right-angled triangle

Worked example

Calculate the length of the unknown side in this triangle.

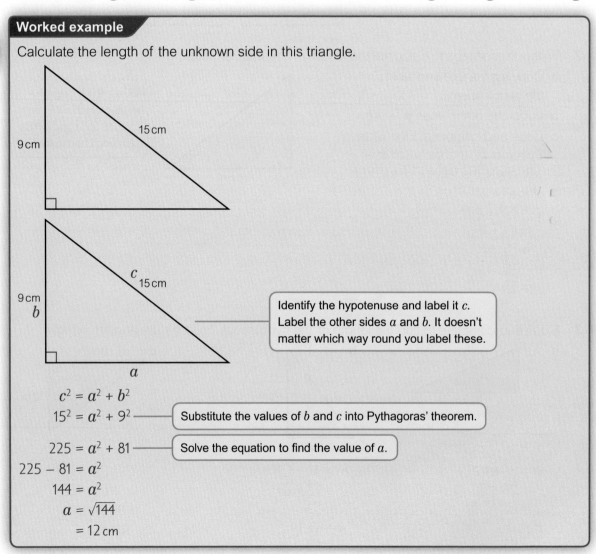

15 cm

9 cm

c 15 cm

9 cm
b

Identify the hypotenuse and label it c. Label the other sides a and b. It doesn't matter which way round you label these.

a

$c^2 = a^2 + b^2$

$15^2 = a^2 + 9^2$ —— Substitute the values of b and c into Pythagoras' theorem.

$225 = a^2 + 81$ —— Solve the equation to find the value of a.

$225 - 81 = a^2$

$144 = a^2$

$a = \sqrt{144}$

$= 12$ cm

1 Copy and complete to find the length of the unknown side in each triangle.

a
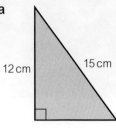

b
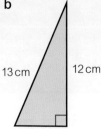

c
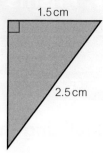

$15^2 = 12^2 + b^2$	$13^2 = \square^2 + b^2$	$\square^2 = \square^2 + \square^2$
$225 = \square + b^2$	$\square = \square + b^2$	$\square = \square + \square$
$225 - \square = b^2$	$\square - \square = b^2$	$\square - \square = \square^2$
$b = \sqrt{\square}$	$b = \sqrt{\square}$	$\square = \sqrt{\square}$
$= \square$ cm	$= \square$ cm	$= \square$ cm

2 **Reasoning** Natalya is calculating the length of the unknown side in the triangle. Here is her working.

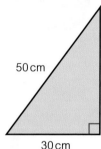

$$c^2 = a^2 + b^2$$
$$= 50^2 + 30^2$$
$$= 2500 + 900$$
$$= 3400$$
$$c = \sqrt{3400}$$
$$= 58.3\text{ cm}$$

a What mistake has Natalya made?

> **Q2a hint** Which side is the hypotenuse?

b Work out the correct length of the unknown side.

Key point   You can rearrange Pythagoras' theorem to find the length of the shorter side:

$$c^2 = a^2 + b^2$$
$$-b^2 \Big(\qquad \Big) -b^2$$
$$c^2 - b^2 = a^2$$

You must make sure that you correctly label the hypotenuse c.

---

3 Complete the calculation to find the length of the unknown side.

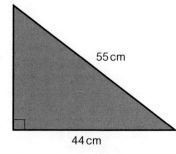

$$a^2 = c^2 - b^2$$
$$= 55^2 - \square^2$$
$$= \square$$
$$a = \sqrt{\square}$$
$$= \square\text{ cm}$$

Reflect   List three important things about Pythagoras' theorem.

7.4 Prisms and cylinders

- Calculate the volume and surface area of a right prism
- Calculate the volume and surface area of a cylinder

Calculating the volume of a right prism

Key point Imagine that a 2D shape with straight edges is stuck to a wall. An identical 2D shape is stuck exactly on to it, and another and another ..., making a 3D solid extending out from the wall.
The 2D shape is called the **cross-section** of the 3D solid.
The 3D solid is called a **right prism**.
These are all right prisms.

Use this formula to calculate the volume of a right prism:
  volume of a right prism = area of cross-section × length

1 Here is a triangular prism. The cross-section is shaded.

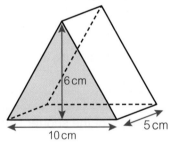

6 cm
10 cm
5 cm

  a Calculate the area of cross-section.

  Q1a hint Area of a triangle = $\frac{1}{2}$ × base × height

  b Work out the volume of the prism using the formula
    volume = area of cross-section × length

  Q1b hint Don't forget the units. Volume is measured in cubic units, e.g. mm³, cm³, m³.

2 Use the method in **Q1** to work out the volume of each of these prisms.
  In each diagram the cross-section has been shaded.

  a
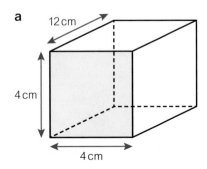
  12 cm
  4 cm
  4 cm

  b
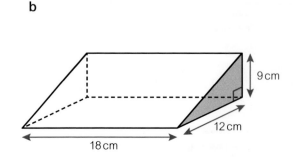
  9 cm
  12 cm
  18 cm

3 This prism has a trapezium as its cross-section. Copy and complete the calculations to work out its volume.

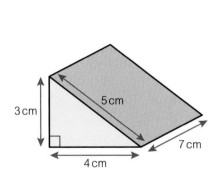

area of cross-section $= \frac{1}{2} \times (\square + \square) \times 8$

$\qquad\qquad\qquad\quad = \frac{1}{2} \times \square \times 8$

$\qquad\qquad\qquad\quad = \square \, cm^2$

volume = area of cross-section × length

$\qquad\qquad\quad = \square \times 10$

$\qquad\qquad\quad = \square \, cm^3$

Calculating the surface area of a right prism

> **Key point** To calculate the surface area of a 3D solid, sketch a net and work out the area of each of the faces.

1 Here is a triangular prism. The net of the prism is shown next to it.

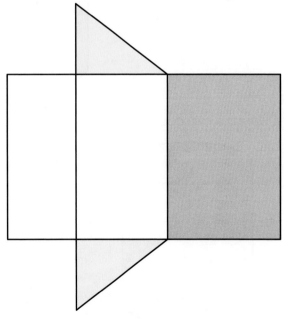

  a Sketch the net.

  b Label the dimensions of each face on the net.

  c Calculate the area of one of the triangles.

  d Calculate the area of the shaded rectangle.

  e Calculate the area of each of the other two rectangular faces.

  f Use your answers to parts **c**, **d** and **e** to calculate the surface area of the triangular prism.

> **Q1f hint** There are **two** triangular faces with the same area.

2 Work out the surface area of this triangular prism. Follow these steps.

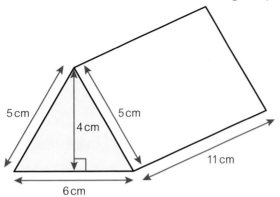

5 cm 5 cm 4 cm 6 cm 11 cm

a Sketch the net of the prism.

b Write the lengths of all the sides on your net.

c Work out the area of each face.

d Add together the areas of each face.

> **Q2c hint** Area of a triangle = $\frac{1}{2}$ × base × height

Calculating the volume and surface area of a cylinder

Volume of a cylinder = area of cross-section × height

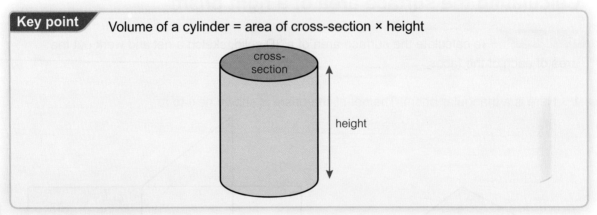

cross-section

height

1 Here is a cylinder.

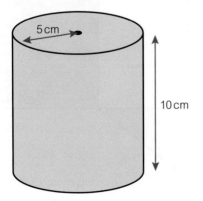

5 cm

10 cm

> **Q1a hint** Area of a circle = π × radius^2

a Calculate the area of the circular cross-section. Round your answer to 1 decimal place.

b Copy and complete. Give your answer to the nearest cm^2.

Volume = area of cross-section × height

$= \square \times 10$

$= \square$ cm^3

2 Use the method in **Q1** to calculate the volume of each cylinder.
Give your answers to 1 decimal place.

a

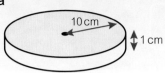

10 cm

1 cm

b

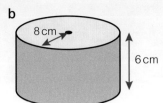

8 cm

6 cm

c

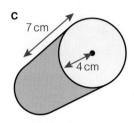

7 cm

4 cm

> **Q2c hint** Think carefully about what the 'height' of the cylinder is.

3 Here is a cylinder and its net.

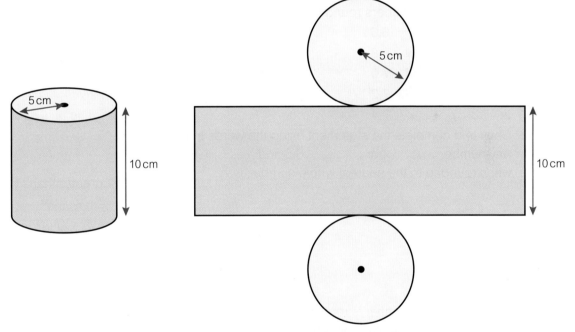

5 cm

10 cm

5 cm

10 cm

10 cm

a Calculate the area of the cross-section. Round your answer to 1 decimal place.

b Calculate the length of the rectangle.
Round your answer to 1 decimal place.

> **Q2b hint** This will be equal to the circumference of the circle. Circumference = $2\pi r$

c Calculate the area of the rectangular part of the net.

d Use your answers to parts **a** and **c** to work out the surface area of the cylinder.
Give your answer to the nearest cm^2.

Reflect Is it easier to calculate the volume or the surface area of right prisms? Explain why.

7.5 Errors and bounds

- Find the lower and upper bounds for a measurement
- Calculate percentage error intervals

Finding upper and lower bounds

Key point This number line shows the inequality $6.5 \leqslant x < 7.5$.

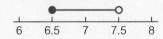

When rounding to the nearest whole number, all the values between 6.5 (including 6.5) and 7.5 round to 7.

Guided

1   **a** Which of these numbers round to 7?

i	6.5	**ii**	6.6
iii	6.7	**iv**	6.8
v	6.9	**vi**	7.0
vii	7.1	**viii**	7.2
ix	7.3	**x**	7.4

   b Copy and complete the statement using the words in the cloud.
   Any number .... or .... 6.5 and 7.5,
   when rounded to the nearest whole number, is 7.

> greater than
> less than
> equal to

Key point When a number is rounded, the **lower bound** is the smallest value it could be. The **upper bound** is the smallest possible value that rounds up to the next number, and is the same as the **lower bound** of the next number.

2   A piece of ribbon is 7 cm to the nearest cm.
   a What is the lower bound of the length?
   b What is the upper bound of the length?

3 Each number has been rounded to the nearest whole number.
The inequalities show the lower and upper bounds.
Write down the lower and upper bound for each number.

a 16

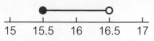

Lower bound = ☐
Upper bound = ☐

b 25

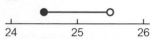

Lower bound = ☐
Upper bound = ☐

4 Each of these numbers has been rounded to the nearest whole number.
For each number

   i copy and complete the number line
   ii draw the inequality
   iii write down the lower and upper bounds.

a 17

Lower bound = ☐
Upper bound = ☐

b 26

```
 |_____|_____|
               26
```

Lower bound = ☐
Upper bound = ☐

c 112

```
 |_____|_____|
              112
```

Lower bound = ☐
Upper bound = ☐

d 205

```
 |_____|_____|
```

Lower bound = ☐
Upper bound = ☐

5 **Reasoning** Explain why there is an 'open' (unshaded) circle on the upper bound of all of your diagrams in **Q4**.

6 Erica rounds the price of a car to £4500 to the nearest £100.

a Copy and complete the number line marked in £100 intervals.

£4400   £4500   [   ]

b On your number line, mark the prices that are the lower and upper bounds.

c Copy and complete the inequality with your lower and upper bounds.

£☐ ⩽ price of car < £☐

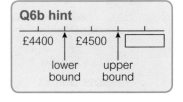

Q6b hint

£4400 ↑ £4500 ↑ [   ]
       lower   upper
       bound   bound

7 Jiang rounds the price of a book to £20 to the nearest £10. Find the lower and upper bounds of the price of the book.

Q7 hint Use the method in **Q6**.

Percentage error intervals

1 **Problem-solving** A factory fills 500 g bags of flour. There is a 10% error interval.

a Copy and complete the number line marked in 100 g intervals.

400 g   500 g   [   ]

b Work out 10% of 500 g.

c Add your answer to part **b** to 500 g. Mark this point on the number line.

d Subtract your answer to part **b** from 500 g. Mark this point on the number line.

e Complete the inequality to show the error interval for the mass of flour.

☐ ⩽ mass of flour < ☐

Q1e hint Look at the number line in part **a**. Which value is 10% below 500 g? Which value is 10% above 500 g?

2 **Problem-solving** The speed of a car is measured as 70 mph.

The speedometer has an error interval of 3%.

a What is the maximum speed at which the car could be travelling?

b What is the minimum speed at which the car could be travelling?

c Write an error interval for the speed of the car.

Q2 hint Draw a number line.

Reflect In this lesson, when did you use the inequality sign for 'less than or equal to'? When did you use the inequality sign for 'less than'?

8 Graphs

8.1 Using $y = mx + c$

- Draw a graph from its equation, without working out points
- Write the equation of a line parallel to another line
- Compare graph lines using their equations

Drawing a graph from its equation

Key point   You can use the gradient and y-intercept to draw a straight-line graph.

1 Follow these steps to draw a straight line with a gradient of 2 and a y-intercept of (0, 1).

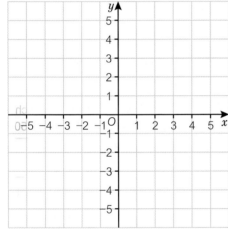

a Copy the coordinate grid.

b Plot the y-intercept (0, 1).

c Put your pencil tip on the y-intercept (0, 1).

   i Draw a dotted line 1 unit right and 2 units up.
      Put a cross at this point.

   ii From your new point, draw a dotted line 1 unit right and 2 units up.
      Put a cross at this new point.

> **Q1c hint** A gradient of 2 means that for every 1 unit right the line goes 2 units up.

d Using a ruler, join the points and continue the line to the edges of the grid.

2 Copy the coordinate grid in **Q1**. On the same grid draw straight-line graphs with

   a a gradient of 3 and y-intercept of (0, 1)

   b a gradient of 1 and y-intercept of (0, −1)

   c a gradient of −2 and y-intercept of (0, 3).

> **Q2c hint**
> For a gradient of −2, go 1 unit right and 2 units down.
>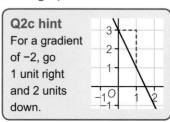

3 For each equation, write down the gradient and the y-intercept. Some parts have been done for you.

    a $y = 5x + 2$ gradient is 5, y-intercept is (0, 2).

    b $y = 7x + 4$ gradient is ☐, y-intercept is (0, ☐).

    c $y = -2x + 3$ gradient is ☐, y-intercept is (☐, ☐).

    d $y = 9x - 1$ gradient is ☐, y-intercept is (☐, ☐).

4 For each equation, write down the gradient and the y-intercept. Then draw the graph and label it. The first part has been done for you.

    a $y = 3x - 2$ gradient is 3, y-intercept is (0, −2).

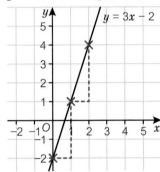

    b $y = -3x + 3$

    c $y = x + 4$

    d $y = 2x - 1$

> **Q4c hint** $y = x + 4$ is the same as $y = 1x + 4$

Parallel lines

1 Match pairs of graphs with the same gradient. One has been done for you.

    a $y = 10x + 2$ **b** $y = -2x - 3$ **c** $y = 5x + 1$ **d** $y = -x - 2$

    i $y = 5x - 2$ **ii** $y = -2x + 2$ **iii** $y = -x + 1$ **iv** $y = 10x - 3$

> **Key point**   Straight lines with the same gradient are **parallel**.

2 These are pairs of equations of parallel lines.
Copy and complete. The first one has been done for you.

    a $y = 5x + 2$ and $y = 5x + 7$

    b $y = -3x + 4$ and $y = ☐ - 2$

    c $y = 2x + 7$ and $y = ☐ + 1$

3 Write the equation of each line. The first one has been done for you.

    a Parallel to the line $y = 7x + 2$ with y-intercept $(0, 4)$: $y = 7x + 4$

    b Parallel to the line $y = -2x + 3$ with y-intercept $(0, 1)$: _____

    c Parallel to the line $y = x - 2$ with y-intercept $(0, -4)$: _____

Intersection of lines

1 Use algebra to work out the coordinates of the point where $y = 5x - 3$ crosses the line $x = 2$.

Substitute $x = 2$ into $y = 5x - 3$.

$y = \Box \times \Box - \Box = \Box - \Box = \Box$

Therefore, $x = \Box$ and $y = \Box$.

So the coordinates are $(\Box, \Box)$.

> **Q1 hint** All points on the line $x = 2$ have x-coordinate 2.

2 **a** Use algebra to work out the coordinates of the point where $y = 2x - 3$ crosses the line $y = 1$.

> **Q2a hint** Follow the steps in **Q1**.

    b The coordinate grid shows the lines $y = 2x - 3$ and $y = 1$. Find the coordinates of the point where the lines cross.

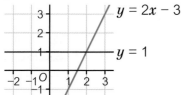

    c What do you notice about your answers to parts **a** and **b**?

3 **Problem-solving** Tabitha says that the line $y = 3x - 5$ passes through the point $(2, 2)$.

    a When $x = 2$, what is the value of $y = 3x - 5$?
Write your answer as coordinates $(2, \Box)$.
What do you notice?

    b Copy the grid and sketch the graph of $y = 3x - 5$.

    c **i** Plot the point $(2, 2)$ on your grid.

        ii Is the point on the line?

    d Is Tabitha correct?

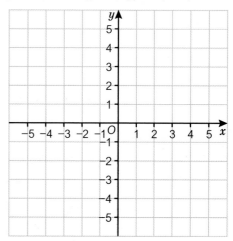

Reflect How many different ways do you know of drawing the graph from an equation of a straight line? Discuss the different methods with a partner.

8.2 More straight-line graphs

- Draw graphs with equations in the form $ax + by = c$
- Rearrange equations of graphs into the form $y = mx + c$

Drawing graphs with equation $ax + by = c$

Key point The point where the graph crosses the x-axis is the x-intercept and always has y-coordinate = 0.
The point where the graph crosses the y-axis is the y-intercept and always has x-coordinate = 0.

1 For the equation $2x + y = 4$

    a work out x when $y = 0$

    b work out y when $x = 0$.

    c Is your answer to part **a** the x-intercept or the y-intercept?

    d Is your answer to part **b** the x-intercept or the y-intercept?

> **Q1a hint** $2x + 0 = 4$

> **Q1b hint** $2 \times 0 + y = 4$

2 For each equation, find the x- and the y-intercepts.

    a $3x + y = 3$ **b** $-2x + y = 2$ **c** $x - y = 7$ **d** $5x - 2y = 10$

> **Q2 hint** Follow the steps in **Q1** parts **a** and **b** to help you.

Guided

3 For each graph, state the coordinates of the x- and the y-intercepts.

    a

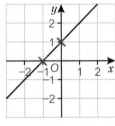

    x-intercept: ($\square$, 0)
    y-intercept: (0, $\square$)

    b

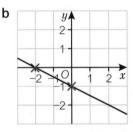

    x-intercept: ($\square$, $\square$)
    y-intercept: ($\square$, $\square$)

    c

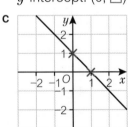

    x-intercept: ($\square$, $\square$)
    y-intercept: ($\square$, $\square$)

4 Copy the coordinate grid. On the same grid, draw straight-line graphs with

  a x-intercept $(2, 0)$ and y-intercept $(0, -1)$

  b x-intercept $(1, 0)$ and y-intercept $(0, 3)$

  c x-intercept $(-3, 0)$ and y-intercept $(0, -2)$

  d x-intercept $(-1, 0)$ and y-intercept $(0, 2)$.

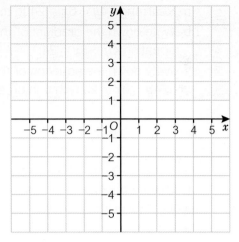

5 **a** Find the x- and the y-intercepts of the graphs with these equations.

Q5 hint Use **Q3** and **Q4** to help you.

    i $y + x = 2$ **ii** $y - x = 3$

    iii $3x - y = 6$ **iv** $-x + 2y = -4$

  b Copy the axes given in **Q4**. Draw the graph of each equation in part **a**.

Working with equations of the form $ax + by = c$

Worked example

For the equation $2x - y = 6$

  a make y the subject

$$2x - y = 6$$
$$-2x \left(\right) -2x$$
$$-y = -2x + 6$$
$$\div(-1) \left(\right) \div(-1)$$
$$y = 2x - 6$$

  b write down the gradient.

    Since $2x - y = 6$ is the same as $y = 2x - 6$ the gradient is 2.

> This is in the form $mx + c$ where the gradient is m.

1 For each equation

  i make y the subject

  ii write down the gradient of its graph.

Q1 hint $y = \square x + \square$
↑
gradient

    a $y - 2x = 7$ **b** $y + 3x = 2$

    c $2y - 4x = 6$ **d** $x - y = 9$

2 Use substitution to check whether the point $(1, 2)$ is on the line with each of these equations.

  a $y - 2x = 0$ **b** $y + x = 1$ **c** $y + x = 3$

3 **Problem-solving**

  a Rearrange $4y - 6x = 24$ to make y the subject.

  b Write down the gradient of the straight-line graph with equation $4y - 6x = 24$.

  c Write down the equation of the line parallel to $4y - 6x = 24$ with y-intercept $(0, 4)$.

Q3b hint Use the gradient from your answer to part **a**.

Q3c hint Remember: parallel lines have the same gradient.
$$y = \square x + \square$$
     ↑   ↑
  gradient y-intercept

4 **Problem-solving** Which pairs of equations have graphs that are parallel to each other? Show your working.

  a $y + x = 2$ and $x + y = -1$

  b $2x + y = 7$ and $y = 2x + 1$

  c $y = 3x + 4$ and $y - 3x = 12$

Q4 hint Rearrange the equations to make y the subject and compare their gradients.

5 **Problem-solving** The equation $5x + 6y = 150$ links the number of hot chocolate sales (y) to the outside temperature (x).

  a Write down the x-intercept and y-intercept of the graph with this equation.

  b Copy the coordinate grid. Draw the line $5x + 6y = 150$.

  c Do hot chocolate sales go up or down as it gets hotter?

  d Use your graph to estimate

    i the number of sales when $x = 10$

    ii the temperature when $y = 20$.

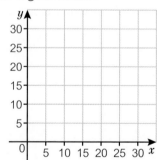

Reflect Explain to a partner how to draw a graph with an equation in the form

  a $y = mx + c$, for example $y = 3x + 1$

  b $ax + by = c$, for example $2x + y = 4$.

Discuss what is the same about your methods for each type of equation. What is different?

8.3 Simultaneous equations

- Solve simultaneous equations by drawing graphs
- Solve problems using simultaneous equations

> **Key point** A pair of **simultaneous equations** have the same x- and y-values.
> This is shown by the **point of intersection** of their graphs.
>
>

Drawing and solving simultaneous equations

1 What is the point of intersection of these graphs of simultaneous equations?

a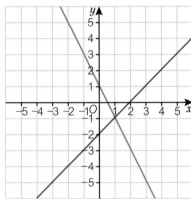

b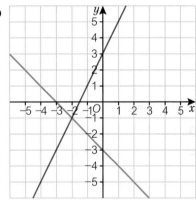

2 $y = x - 3$ and $y = -3x + 1$ are a pair of simultaneous equations.

a For the graph of the first equation, $y = x - 3$, write down

   i the gradient   **ii** the y-intercept.

b For the graph of the second equation, $y = -3x + 1$, write down

   i the gradient   **ii** the y-intercept.

c Copy the coordinate grid.
On the same grid, draw the graphs of the two equations.

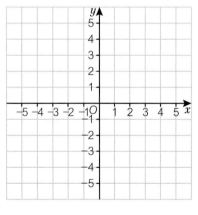

> **Q2c hint** Use parts **a** and **b** to help you.

d Find the point of intersection of the two graphs.

e Using your answer to part **d**, copy and complete the solution to the simultaneous equations.

   $x = \square$ and $y = \square$

f Check your solution by substituting back into one of the equations.

Guided

3 Draw graphs to solve these pairs of simultaneous equations.

a $y = 4x - 2$
$y = -x + 3$

b $y = 3x + 1$
$y = -2x - 4$

Q3 hint Follow the steps in **Q2** to help you.

4 $x - 2y = 1$ and $3x + y = 3$ are a pair of simultaneous equations.

a For the graph of the first equation, $x - 2y = 1$, write down

   i the gradient   **ii** the y-intercept.

b For the graph of the second equation, $3x + y = 3$, write down

   i the gradient   **ii** the y-intercept.

c Copy the coordinate grid. On the same grid, draw the graphs of the two equations.

d Find the point of intersection of the two graphs.

e Using your answer from part **d**, copy and complete the solution to the simultaneous equations.

   $x = \square$ and $y = \square$

f Check your solution by substituting back into one of the equations.

5 Draw graphs to solve these simultaneous equations.

a $x + y = 2$
$x - 2y = 5$

b $x + 3y = 5$
$y - 2x = 4$

Q5 hint Follow the steps in **Q4** to help you.

6 Draw graphs to solve the simultaneous equations $y = x$ and $x - 5y = 4$.

Q6 hint Find the x- and the y-intercepts for the graph of each equation. Then use these to draw the graphs.

Solving problems with simultaneous equations

1 **Problem-solving** Kat walks along the path $y = x - 4$. Tom walks along the path $x + y = 2$.

a Draw a coordinate grid with both axes from −6 to 6. Then draw the paths for Kat and Tom.

b Use your graphs to find the coordinates where their paths cross.

2 **Problem-solving** Two numbers added together make 10. Their difference is 2.

a Write down two equations using x and y to represent the two numbers.

   Equation 1: $\square + \square = \square$ Equation 2: $\square - \square = \square$

Q2a hint
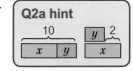

b Find the x- and the y-intercepts of the graphs of both equations.

c Draw graphs to solve the simultaneous equations.

Q2c hint Look at the x- and y-intercepts from part **b** to help you draw the coordinate grid.

Guided

Guided

3 Problem-solving At the theatre, the number of child tickets sold is x and the number of adult tickets sold is y.

a Copy and complete this expression for the total number of tickets sold: $\Box + \Box$.

The total number sold is 40.

b Copy and complete this equation for the total number sold: $\Box + \Box = \Box$.

A child ticket costs £5 and an adult ticket costs £8.

c Copy and complete this expression for the amount of money taken for tickets: $\Box x + \Box y$.

The total amount of money taken for tickets is £290.

d Copy and complete the equation for the total amount of money taken for tickets: $\Box x + \Box y = \Box$.

e Copy the coordinate grid.

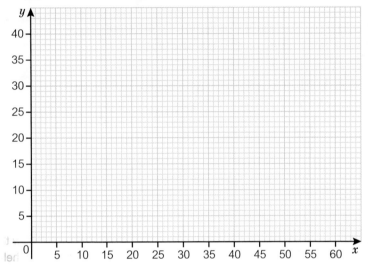

f Find the point of intersection of the graphs.

Q3f hint Draw the graphs of the equations in parts **b** and **d**.

g Find x, the number of child tickets sold, and y, the number of adult tickets sold.

4 Problem-solving At a concert, the number of t-shirts sold is x, and the number of hoodies sold is y.

Q4 hint Use **Q3** to help you.

a The total number of t-shirts and hoodies sold is 14. Write an equation to represent this.

A t-shirt costs £7 and a hoodie costs £15.

b The total amount of money taken for sales of t-shirts and hoodies is £130. Write an equation to represent this.

c Draw a coordinate grid with both axes from 0 to 25. Draw the graphs of the equations in parts **a** and **b**.

d Using the point of intersection, find the number of t-shirts and the number of hoodies sold.

Reflect Look back at **Q2** in the section on solving problems. What clues are there in the question that tell you that you need to solve a pair of simultaneous equations?

8.4 Graphs of quadratic functions

- Draw graphs with quadratic equations like $y = x^2$
- Interpret graphs of quadratic functions

Graphs of quadratic equations

Key point In a **quadratic equation** you will always see an x^2 term. For example, these are all quadratic equations:

$y = x^2$ $y = 2x^2$ $y = x^2 + 1$

You will never see an x term with a higher power in a quadratic equation.

The graph of a quadratic equation is a curve called a **parabola**.

Guided

1 Work out each calculation for the equation $y = x^2$. The first one has been done for you.

    a $x = -2$: $y = (-2)^2 = -2 \times -2 = 4$

    b $x = -1$: $y = (-1)^2 = \square \times \square = \square$

    c $x = 0$: $y = (0)^2 = \square \times \square = \square$

    d $x = 1$: $y = (1)^2 = \square \times \square = \square$

Guided

2   **a** For the equation $y = x^2$, copy and complete the table of values. Some parts have been done for you.

> **Q2a hint** Use **Q1** to help.

x	-3	-2	-1	0	1	2	3
y	$(-3)^2 = 9$	$(-2)^2 = \square$	$(\square)^2 = \square$	$(\square)^2 = \square$	$(\square)^2 = \square$	$(2)^2 = 4$	$(\square)^2 = \square$

    b Copy and complete these coordinate pairs from the table.

    $(-3, \square)$, $(-2, \square)$, $(-1, \square)$, $(0, \square)$, $(1, \square)$, $(2, \square)$, $(3, \square)$

    c Copy the coordinate grid. On your grid, plot the points from part **b**.
Join the points with a smooth curve.
Label the curve with its equation.

> **Q2c hint**
> Shape of graph is

    d Is the graph symmetrical? If so, draw a coloured dotted line to show the line of symmetry.

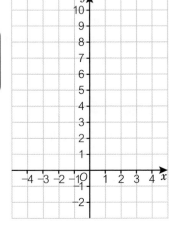

3 Work out each calculation for the equation $y = 2x^2$.
The first one has been done for you.

a $x = -2$: $y = 2(-2)^2 = 2 \times -2 \times -2 = 8$
b $x = -1$: $y = 2(-1)^2 = 2 \times \square \times \square = \square$
c $x = 0$: $y = 2(0)^2 = \square \times \square \times \square = \square$
d $x = 1$: $y = 2(1)^2 = \square \times \square \times \square = \square$

4 **a** Copy and complete the table of values for the equation $y = 2x^2$.
Some parts have been done for you.

x	−3	−2	−1	0	1	2	3
y	$2(-3)^2 = 18$	$2(-2)^2 = \square$	$2(\square)^2 = \square$	$2(\square)^2 = \square$	$2(\square)^2 = \square$	$2(2)^2 = 8$	$2(\square)^2 = \square$

b Copy and complete these coordinate pairs from the table.
$(-3, \square)$, $(-2, \square)$, $(-1, \square)$, $(0, \square)$, $(1, \square)$, $(2, \square)$, $(3, \square)$

c Copy the coordinate grid.
On your grid, plot the points from part **b**.
Join the points with a smooth curve.
Label the curve with its equation.

d Is the graph symmetrical? If so, draw a coloured
dotted line to show the line of symmetry.

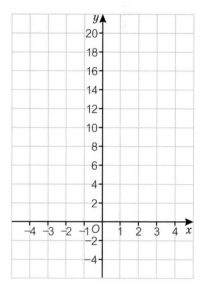

5 **Reasoning** Write true or false for each statement.
a Graphs of quadratic equations are straight lines.
b Graphs of quadratic equations are symmetrical.
c Graphs of quadratic equations are parabolas.
d This is a graph of a quadratic function:

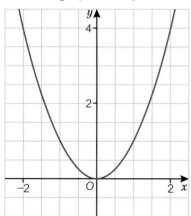

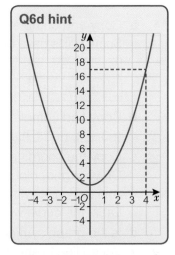

6 a Copy and complete the table for the equation $y = x^2 + 1$.
Some parts have been done for you.

x	−3	−2	−1	0	1	2	3
x^2	$(-3)^2 = 9$		$(-1)^2 = 1$			$2^2 = 4$	
$+1$	$+1$	$+1$	$+1$	$+1$	$+1$	$+1$	$+1$
y	$9 + 1 = 10$		$1 + 1 = 2$			$4 + 1 = \square$	

b Write down the coordinate pairs from the table.
The first is (−3, 10).

c Copy the coordinate grid in **Q4**.
On your grid, plot the coordinate points from part **b**.
Join the points with a smooth curve.
Label the curve with its equation.

d Using your graph, estimate the value of y when x is 4.

Q6d hint

Problem-solving using graphs of quadratic equations

1 Problem-solving The graph shows the path of a football after it has been kicked.

a What distance does the ball travel?

b Find the height when the ball has reached a distance of 30 m.

c What is the maximum (greatest) height the ball reaches?

d What distance has the ball travelled when it reaches its maximum height?

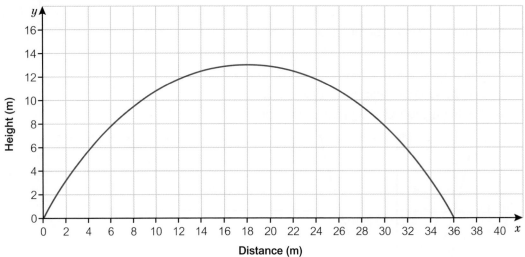

Distance (m)

Reflect Write a list of the new things you have learned this lesson. Compare your list with a partner's list.

8.5 More non-linear graphs

- Draw and interpret graphs showing inverse proportion
- Draw and interpret non-linear graphs

Drawing and interpreting non-linear graphs

Key point   A **non-linear** graph is a graph that is not a straight line.

1 **Reasoning**   Which of these graphs are non-linear?

A	B	C	D
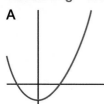	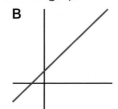	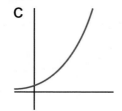	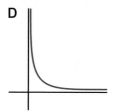

2 **a** For this non-linear graph find

   i the value of y when x is 5   **ii** the value of x when $y = 2$.

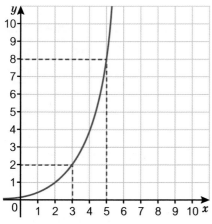

   b For this non-linear graph find

   i the value of x when $y = 9$ **ii** the value of y when x is 5.

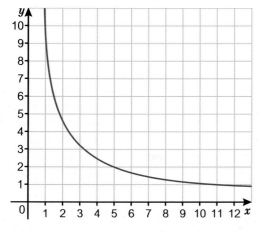

Drawing and interpreting graphs showing inverse proportion

1 Here is the graph of an equation in the form $y = \frac{k}{x}$.

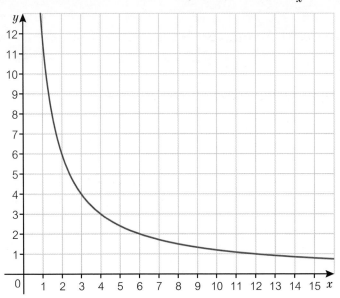

a Copy and complete the table of values by reading values from the graph.

x	1	2	3	4	6	
y	12			3		1

Q1a hint When $x = 2$, find the value of y.

b Substitute $x = 1$ and $y = 12$ into the equation $y = \frac{k}{x}$ and work out the value of k.

c Copy and complete the equation of the graph: $y = \frac{\square}{x}$

Q1c hint Use the value of k you found in part **b**.

d Substitute $x = 4$ and $y = 3$ into the equation to check your answer.

e Find the value of y when $x = 24$.

Q1e hint Use the equation of the graph from part **c**.

2 The graph shows the time in hours it takes to paint a room as the number of painters changes.

a Copy the table of values and use the graph to complete it.

Time (hours)	1	2	
Number of painters			1

Time taken to paint a room

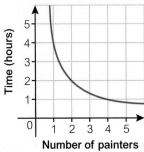

b The graph has the equation: time = $\dfrac{k}{\text{number of painters}}$
Find the value of k.

Q2b hint Substitute a pair of values from your table to work out k. Check your answer with a different pair of values from your table.

c Find the number of painters needed to paint a room in half an hour.

113

3 Problem-solving The table shows the population of rabbits at different time intervals.

Time (months)	0	1	2	3	4
Number of rabbits	1	2	4	8	16

a Look at the pattern for the number of rabbits. How many rabbits will there be after 5 months?

b Copy and complete the coordinate pairs for the time and the number of rabbits.
(0, 1), (1, □), (2, □), (3, □), (4, □), (5, □)

c Copy the coordinate grid, title and axis labels. On your grid, plot the coordinate points from part **b**.
Join the points with a smooth curve.

d Estimate the time it will take for there to be 12 rabbits.

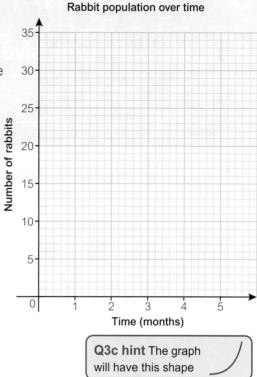

Q3c hint The graph will have this shape

4 Problem-solving The graph shows the value of a car in £1000s over a period of time.

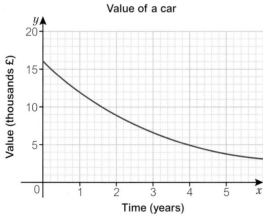

a What was the value of the car when it was new?

b Find the value after 1 year.

c How long did it take for the value to be £5000?

d Use your answer to part **a** to work out how long it took for the car to halve in value.

Q4a hint When the car was new, time = 0. When time = 0, value = □. Write your answer in thousands of pounds.

Q4c hint When value = £5000, time = □ years

Q4d hint When value = half of answer to part **a**, time = □.

Reflect What types of equations and graphs have you learned about in this unit?
Draw an example for each type of equation and graph. Compare your examples with a partner's.

9 Probability

9.1 Mutually exclusive events

- Identify mutually exclusive outcomes and events
- Work out the probabilities of mutually exclusive outcomes and events

Mutually exclusive outcomes and events

1   There are 2 grey cards and 5 white cards. Each card has a square or a circle.

   a How many cards show a circle?

   b How many cards show a square?

   A card is picked at random. Write down the probability that the card

   c has a circle

   d has a square

   e is grey

   f has a circle *or* is a white card

   g has a square *and* is a grey card.

> **Q1f hint** Count the number of cards that either have a circle or are white.

> **Q1g hint** Count the number of cards that have a square and are grey.

2   List the possible outcomes for each event when rolling a normal 6-sided dice.

The first two have been done for you.

   a Rolling a 5
     1 2 3 4 ⑤ 6

   b Rolling an even number
     1 ② 3 ④ 5 ⑥

   c Rolling an odd number
     1 2 3 4 5 6

   d Rolling a multiple of 3
     1 2 3 4 5 6

   e Rolling a factor of 6
     1 2 3 4 5 6

   f Rolling a factor of 4
     1 2 3 4 5 6

3   Look at your answers to **Q2**.

   a Do rolling an even number and rolling an odd number have any outcomes in common?

   b **Reasoning** Are rolling an even number and rolling an odd number **mutually exclusive**? Explain.

> **Q3b hint** Two events are **mutually exclusive** if they have no outcomes in common.

4   Look at your answers to **Q2** again. Which of these events are mutually exclusive?

   A Rolling an even number and rolling a factor of 6

   B Rolling a multiple of 3 and rolling a factor of 4

   C Rolling a 5 and rolling a factor of 6

5 10 balls are placed in a bag. 5 balls are red, 2 are yellow and 3 are blue.
Tina picks a ball at random.

  a Work out
    i P(R)   **ii** P(Y)   **iii** P(B)

  b Work out
    i P(R or Y)   **ii** P(R or B)   **iii** P(B or Y)

> **Q5ai hint** P(R) means the probability of picking red.

> **Q5bi hint** P(R or Y) means the probability of picking red or yellow.

  c Reasoning Explain why the outcomes red, yellow and blue are mutually exclusive.

  d Copy and complete.
    i P(R or Y) = ☐, P(R) + P(Y) = ☐ + ☐ = ☐   **ii** P(R or B) = ☐, P(R) + P(B) = ☐ + ☐ = ☐
    iii P(B or Y) = ☐, P(B) + P(Y) = ☐ + ☐ = ☐

  e Reasoning What do you notice about the probability of one event or another, when the two events are mutually exclusive?

Probabilities of mutually exclusive outcomes and events

1 The table shows the probabilities that a traffic light is red, amber or green.

Traffic light	Red	Amber	Green
Probability	45%	7%	48%

  a Work out the total of the percentages.
  b Write each percentage as a decimal. The first one has been done for you.
    i 45% = 0.45   **ii** 7% = ☐   **iii** 48% = ☐
  c Work out the total of the decimals.

2 A different traffic light has these probabilities that the light is red, amber or green.
Copy and complete.
35% + 5% + ☐% = 100%
40% + ☐% = 100%
P(G) = ☐%

Traffic light	Red	Amber	Green
Probability	35%	5%	☐%

3 A restaurant has 4 different dessert specials: apple pie, chocolate cake, ice cream, and strawberries and cream. The probability that each one is on the menu is shown in the table.

Dessert	Apple pie	Chocolate cake	Ice cream	Strawberries and cream
Probability	☐ %	0.45	0.25	0.15

  a Add up the probabilities of chocolate cake, ice cream, and strawberries and cream.
  b What is the probability that apple pie is on the menu?

Reflect Look at the spinner.
Use what you have learned about mutually exclusive events to explain why getting a red and getting an odd number are not mutually exclusive events.

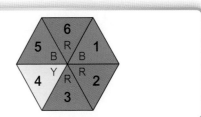

9.2 Experimental and theoretical probability

- Calculate estimates of probability from experiments
- Decide whether a dice or spinner is unbiased

Probability from experiments

1   Jessica spins a spinner. She records the number it lands on in a frequency table.

Number	1	2	3	4	5
Tally	卌 卌 卌 IIII	卌 卌 卌 卌 卌	卌 卌 卌 卌	卌 卌 IIII	卌 卌 卌 卌 II
Frequency	19	25	20	14	22

a   Work out the total number of spins.

b   How many times does the spinner land on 1?

c   What is the **experimental probability** of landing on a 1?

d   How many times does the spinner land on 5?

e   What is the probability of landing on a 5?

f   Which outcome is the most likely?

g   Which outcome is the least likely?

> **Q1c hint** Experimental probability =
> $\dfrac{\text{number of times the spinner lands on 1}}{\text{total number of spins}}$

> **Q1f hint** Which number does the spinner land on most often?

2   Predict how many times the same spinner would land on the number 3 if Jessica spins it

a   200 times

```
    spins  number 3
    100       20
×□ (          ) ×□
    200       □
```

b   500 times

```
    spins  number 3
    100       20
×□ (          ) ×□
    500       □
```

c   1000 times.

```
    spins  number 3
    100       20
×□ (          ) ×□
    1000      □
```

3 Jessica continues to spin the spinner. Write down how many times she should expect to spin it so that it lands on the number 2

a 50 times

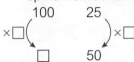

spins number 2
100   25
×☐ ( ) ×☐
    ☐   50

b 100 times

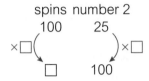

spins number 2
100   25
×☐ ( ) ×☐
    ☐   100

c 250 times.

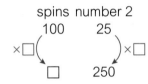

spins number 2
100   25
×☐ ( ) ×☐
    ☐   250

4 **a** What is the probability of the spinner landing on red?
b What is the probability of the spinner landing on blue?
c **Reasoning** Robert says there are two colours on the spinner, so it is equally likely to land on red or blue.
Explain why Robert is wrong.

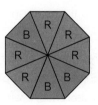

5 Here are three spinners.

Spinner A

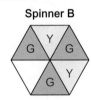

Spinner B

Spinner C

a Copy and complete for spinner A.
  i Spinner A has ☐ red sections and ☐ blue sections.
  ii The probability of spinner A landing on red is ☐ and on blue is ☐.
  iii Landing on red and landing on blue <u>are / are not</u> equally likely.
b **Problem-solving** Freya wants to make it equally likely that spinner B will land on green or yellow. What colour should she choose for the final section?
c **Problem-solving** Jose wants to make it 5 times more likely that spinner C will land on purple than orange. What colour should he choose for the final section?

Comparing experimental and theoretical probabilities

1 Lewis spins this spinner 100 times and records the results in a table.

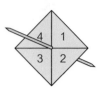

Score	Frequency	Experimental probability	Theoretical probability
1	28	0.28	
2	21		
3	23		
4	28		

a Write down the experimental probability of the spinner landing on

　i 1 　$\frac{28}{100} = 0.28$ 　**ii** 2 　**iii** 3 　**iv** 4

　Give your answer as a decimal. The first one has been done for you.

b Copy the table and complete the experimental probability column.

c Write down the theoretical probability of the spinner landing on

　i 1 　$\frac{1}{4} = \square$ 　**ii** 2 　**iii** 3 　**iv** 4

　Give your answer as a decimal. The first one has been started for you.

d Complete the theoretical probability column.

2 The table shows the numbers of heads recorded when Ana flipped 3 different coins 100 times each.

Coin	A	B	C
Number of heads	45	56	23
Experimental probability			
Theoretical probability			

a Copy the table. Work out the experimental probability of landing on heads for each coin.

b What is the theoretical probability of an **unbiased** coin landing on heads?

c How many heads would you expect if an unbiased coin were flipped 100 times?

d Which coins have experimental probability close to the theoretical probability?

e Which coins have their number of heads close to the expected number of heads?

f **Reasoning** Which coin might be biased? Explain your answer.

> **Q2f hint** A coin is unbiased if the theoretical probability is close to the experimental probability.

3 **Problem-solving / Reasoning** Simon spins 3 different spinners 100 times each. The number of times they land on red is recorded in the table.

Spinner A 　　Spinner B 　　Spinner C

Spinner			
Number of times landed on red	46	52	63

Which results do you think come from which spinner?

> **Reflect** In **Q3** above, can you be certain which spinner gave which result?
> Discuss your answers with a partner.

9.3 Sample space diagrams

- List all the possible outcomes of one or two events in a sample space diagram
- Decide if a game is fair

Drawing sample space diagrams

1 Write all the possible outcomes when

  a a coin is flipped

  b a 6-sided dice is rolled

  c this spinner is spun.

2 These two spinners are spun at the same time.

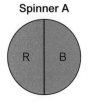

  a Copy and complete this list of possible outcomes.

  b How many different outcomes are there?

  c How many outcomes are red on spinner A and purple on spinner B?

  d Work out the probability of getting red on spinner A and purple on spinner B.

Spinner A	Spinner B
red	yellow
red	☐
blue	☐
blue	purple

3 Sean rolls two fair 6-sided dice. He records whether the number rolled on each dice is even or odd.

  a Copy and complete this list of possible outcomes.

Blue dice	Red dice	Outcome
even	even	E, E
even	☐	E, ☐
odd	☐	O, ☐
odd	☐	☐, ☐

  b How many outcomes give one even number and one odd number?

  c What is the probability of getting one even number and one odd number when two dice are rolled?

4 Copy the sample space diagram and use your answers to **Q3** to complete it to show all possible outcomes.

5 Josie flips a coin and spins a spinner.

a Copy and complete the table to show all the possible outcomes. Some parts have been done for you.

Spinner	Coin
1	H
☐	H
☐	H
1	T
☐	☐
☐	☐

b Copy and complete the sample space diagram showing all the possible outcomes.

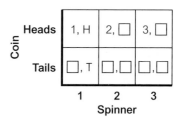

Probability from a sample space diagram

1 The sample space diagram shows the possible outcomes when a coin is flipped and a dice is rolled.

a What is the total number of possible outcomes?

b How many outcomes have Tails, T?

c What is the probability of getting Tails?

d How many outcomes have Even and Heads?

e What is the probability of getting Even and Heads?

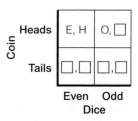

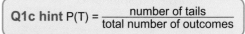
Q1c hint $P(T) = \dfrac{\text{number of tails}}{\text{total number of outcomes}}$

2 These dominoes are placed face down.
Candice picks one domino from each set.
She writes down the total number of spots on both dominoes.

Set A   Set B

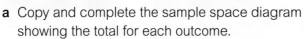

a Copy and complete the sample space diagram showing the total for each outcome.

b What is the total number of possible outcomes?

c How many outcomes have a total score of 3?

d What is the probability of getting a total score of 3?

e How many outcomes have a total score of an even number?

f What is the probability of getting a total score that is even?

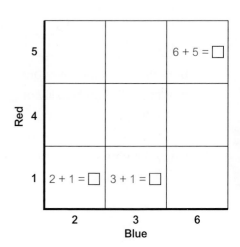

Deciding if a game is fair

1 Some friends roll two 4-sided dice together 100 times and add their scores.

a Copy and complete the sample space diagram showing the total for each outcome. Some have been started for you.

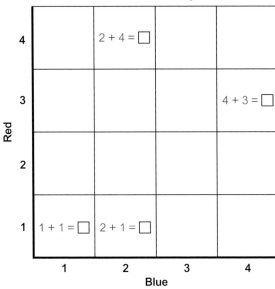

b Work out
  i P(even)   **ii** P(odd).

Louis and Ryan play a game where Louis wins if the total is even and Ryan wins if the total is odd.

c Which person is more likely to win this game: Louis or Ryan?

d **Reasoning** Is this game fair? Explain.

> **Q1d hint** A game is 'fair' if all players have the same probability of winning.

e Work out
  i P(multiple of 5)
  ii P(not a multiple of 5).

Ruth and Virat play a game where Ruth wins if the total is a multiple of 5 and Virat wins if the total is not a multiple of 5.

f **Reasoning** Is this a fair game? Explain.

Reflect Look back at the section 'Drawing sample space diagrams'. In **Q5** you listed all the outcomes and then drew a sample space diagram. In later questions you drew the sample space diagram without listing the outcomes first. Which method do you think is more useful? Explain.

9.4 Two-way tables

- Show all the possible outcomes of two events in a two-way table
- Calculate probabilities from two-way tables

Reading a two-way table

Guided

1 Spinner A and Spinner B are both spun 100 times. The results are shown in a two-way table.

		Spinner B		
		Blue	Red	Total
Spinner A	Green	30	24	30 + 24 = ☐
	Yellow	22	24	22 + 24 = ☐
	Total	30 + 22 = ☐	24 + 24 = ☐	100

  a Copy and complete the table by working out the totals.

  b How many times did spinner A land on green?

  c How many times did spinner B land on red?

  d How many times did spinner A land on yellow and spinner B land on blue?

  e Which combination of colours occurred 30 times?

Calculating probabilities from a two-way table

1 The table shows some information about a group of 14-year-old students.

		Year group		
		Year 9	Year 10	Total
Dominant hand	Right	61	29	90
	Left	4	6	10
	Total	65	35	100

  a How many students are there in total?

  b How many students are right-handed?

  c A student is picked at random. What is the probability that the student is right-handed?

  d How many students are in Year 9?

  e A student is picked at random. What is the probability that the student is in Year 9?

  f How many students are in Year 9 and are left-handed?

  g A student is picked at random. What is the probability that the student is a Year 9 student who is left-handed?

  h How many left-handed Year 10 students are there?

  i A student is picked at random. What is the probability that the student is a Year 10 student who is left-handed?

> **Q1h hint** 'Left-handed Year 10' means the student is in Year 10 **and** is left-handed.

2 The table shows some information about Year 7, 8 and 9 students and whether or not they eat breakfast.

		Do you eat breakfast?		
		Yes	No	Total
Year group	Year 7	53	19	
	Year 8	39	24	
	Year 9	34	31	
	Total			

a Copy and complete the two-way table by working out the totals.

b How many students are there in Year 8?

c How many Year 8 students do not eat breakfast?

A student is picked at random from Year 8.

d Work out the probability that a student picked at random from Year 8 does not eat breakfast.

e How many students eat breakfast?

f How many students who eat breakfast are in Year 7?

A student who eats breakfast is picked at random.

g What is the probability that this student is in Year 7?

3 Macy spins these two spinners at the same time.

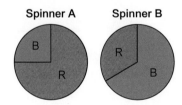

Spinner A   Spinner B

a Copy and complete the two-way table by filling in the totals.

		Spinner B		
		Red	Blue	Total
Spinner A	Red	14	26	
	Blue	3	7	
	Total			50

b How many times did Macy spin the spinners?

c How many times did both spinners land on red?

d What is the experimental probability that both spinners land on red?

e How many times did one spinner land on red and the other spinner land on blue?

> **Q3e hint** This can happen in two different ways.

f What is the experimental probability of one spinner landing on red and the other on blue?

g What is the experimental probability that both spinners land on blue?

4 Dimitri asks 20 students in Year 9 whether they have read a book and/or seen a film in the last month.

		Book		
		Yes	No	Total
Film	Yes	2	9	
	No	3	6	
	Total			20

a Copy and complete the two-way table by working out the totals.

b Work out the probability that a student picked at random has

  i seen a film

  ii not seen a film.

c **Reasoning** A student is picked at random. Is it more likely that this student has seen a film or has not seen a film? Explain.

d How many students have not read a book and not seen a film?

e There are 200 students in Year 9.
Estimate how many students have not read a book and have not seen a film.

Q4e hint

Not read book and not seen film	People
6	20
	200

×☐ (   ) ×☐

☐

Reflect   Becca says the hardest part of two-way tables is understanding the question.
Oleg says the hardest part is working out the probabilities.
Who do you agree with? Explain your answer to a partner.

9.5 Venn diagrams

- Draw Venn diagrams
- Calculate probabilities from Venn diagrams

Reading a Venn diagram

1 **Reasoning** The Venn diagram shows two events when a 6-sided dice is rolled: prime numbers and multiples of 2.

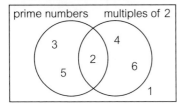

a Copy and complete.
The prime numbers in the diagram are □, □ and □.
The multiples of 2 in the diagram are □, □ and □.

b Why is 2 placed where the circles overlap?

c Explain why the two events are not mutually exclusive.

d Why is 1 outside the circles?

Q1a hint

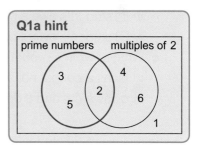

Probability from a Venn diagram

1 The Venn diagram shows two events when a 6-sided dice is rolled: even numbers and numbers greater than 3.

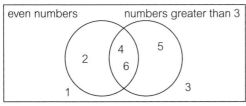

a How many numbers are in the diagram?

b How many even numbers are in the diagram?

c What is the probability of rolling an even number?

d What is the probability of rolling an even number or a number greater than 3?

e How many even numbers are also greater than 3?

f What is the probability of rolling an even number that is also greater than 3?

Q2d hint

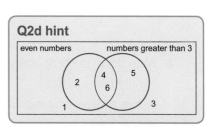

Q2e hint

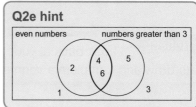

Drawing Venn diagrams and calculating probabilities

Guided

1 The Venn diagram shows the number of students who own a dog, own a cat, own both or own neither.

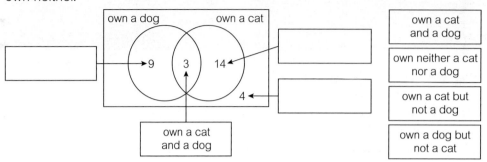

own a cat and a dog

own neither a cat nor a dog

own a cat but not a dog

own a dog but not a cat

own a cat and a dog

   a Copy the diagram and add the labels. The first one has been done for you.
   b Copy and complete.
   i There are 9 + 3 + ☐ + ☐ = ☐ students in the Venn diagram.
   ii ☐ students own a cat but not a dog.   iii ☐ students own a cat.
   iv ☐ students own a cat and a dog.   v ☐ students own neither a cat nor a dog.
   c Write down the probability that a student picked at random
   i owns a cat but not a dog   ii owns a cat
   iii owns a cat and a dog   iv owns neither a cat nor a dog.

   Q1c hint Use your answers to part **b**.

2 In a class of 25 students, 12 students have a sister, 11 students have a brother and 5 students have both a sister and a brother.
   a How many people have only a sister?
   b How many people have only a brother?
   c How many people have neither a sister nor a brother?
   d Copy and complete the Venn diagram.

   Q2a hint

   sister   brother

   ☐   5   ☐

   ☐

   12 students have a sister, so ☐ + 5 = 12.
   11 students have a brother, so ☐ + 5 = 11.

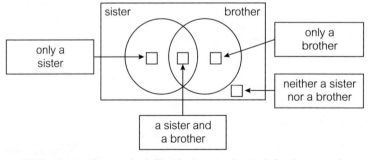

only a sister

only a brother

neither a sister nor a brother

a sister and a brother

   Q2c hint There are 25 people in the class in total, so the numbers in the diagram must total 25.

   e Write down the probability that a student picked at random
   i only has a sister
   ii has a sister and a brother
   iii only has a sister or only has a brother.

Reflect   Look back at your answers to **Q2** above. Write down steps for the order in which to draw and complete a Venn diagram.

10 Comparing shapes

10.1 Congruent and similar shapes

- Use congruent shapes to solve problems about triangles and other polygons
- Work out whether shapes are similar, congruent or neither

Congruent and similar shapes

1 Write down the letter of the rectangle that is
   a the same size as rectangle A
   b an enlargement of rectangle A.

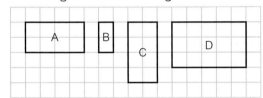

> **Q1a hint** You can trace rectangle A.
> Then rotate the tracing paper and lay it over rectangles B, C and D to help you decide.

2 Write down the letters of the pairs of rectangles in **Q1** that are
   a congruent
   b similar.

> **Q2a hint** Two shapes are **congruent** if they are exactly the same shape and size.

> **Q2b hint** Two shapes are **similar** if one is an enlargement of the other.

Guided

3 Follow these steps to find out whether triangles ABC and DEF are similar.

   a On squared paper, use a ruler to draw triangle DEF in the same orientation as triangle ABC. Use DE as the base of the triangle.

   b Label the vertices of the new triangle correctly with the letters DEF.

   c Label the side lengths of the new triangle.

   d Side AB corresponds to side DE.
   Write down the side that corresponds to side
   i AC ii BC

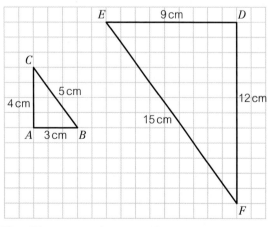

   e Work out the ratio between corresponding sides. Copy and complete the calculations.

   Length of side $DE \div$ length of side $AB = 9 \div \square = \square$.
   Length of side $DF \div$ length of side $\square = 12 \div \square = \square$.
   Length of side $EF \div$ length of side $\square = \square \div \square = \square$.

   f **Reasoning** Are triangles ABC and DEF similar? Explain how you know.

> **Q3f hint** Shapes are similar when the ratio between the lengths of corresponding sides is constant.

4   **Reasoning**   For each pair of shapes, decide whether they are
- congruent
- similar
- neither.

Explain how you know.

a

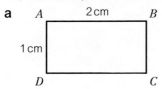
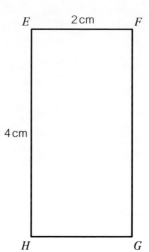

Q4 hint You can use tracing paper and the steps in **Q3** to help you.

b

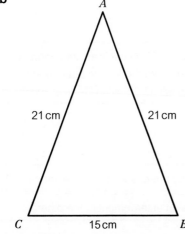
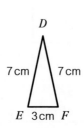

c

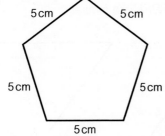

d

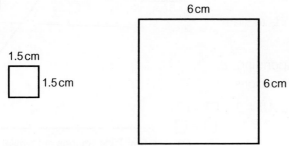

Using congruent shapes to solve problems

1 These two triangles are congruent.

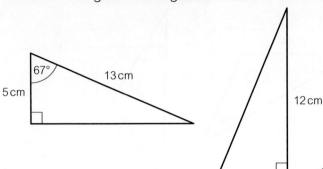

a Copy the triangles.

b Mark on the lengths of all the sides.

c Mark on the size of each angle in both triangles.

> **Q1b hint** Congruent shapes are exactly the same shape and size.

> **Q1c hint** Angles in a triangle sum to 180°.

2 a Triangles are congruent if all three sides are equal (Side, Side, Side, or SSS).
Which of these triangles are congruent because of SSS?

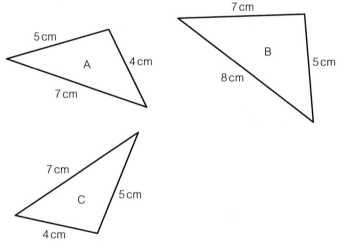

b Triangles are congruent if two sides and the angle **between them** are equal (Side, Angle, Side, or SAS).
Which of these triangles are congruent because of SAS?

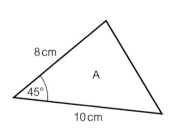
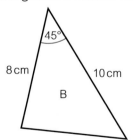

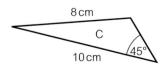

c Triangles are congruent if two angles and the side **between them** are equal
(Angle, Side, Angle, or ASA).
Which of these triangles are congruent because of ASA?

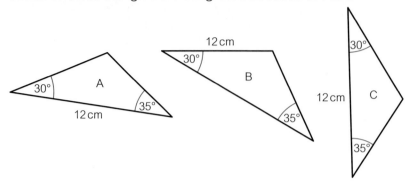

d Triangles are congruent if two angles and a non-included side are equal
(Angle, Angle, Side, or AAS).
Which of these triangles are congruent because of AAS?

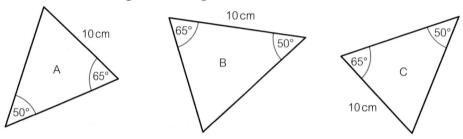

3 Reasoning Adaku says, 'These two triangles are congruent because they both have one
side measuring 10 cm and one angle of 90°'.
Explain why Adaku is wrong.

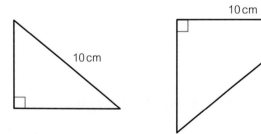

> **Q3 hint** Look carefully at the
> sides labelled 10 cm in each
> triangle. Are they in the same
> position on each triangle?

4 Reasoning
a Use a ruler to draw a square with side length 5 cm.
b Use a ruler to draw another square. Choose your own side length.
c Are your two squares similar?
d Are all squares similar? Explain your answer.

Reflect The words **congruent** and **similar** have different meanings.
Write a sentence describing what each word means in maths. Use diagrams to illustrate
your descriptions.

10.2 Ratios in triangles

- Solve problems involving similar triangles

Sides in similar triangles

1 Two triangles *ABC* and *DEF* are similar.

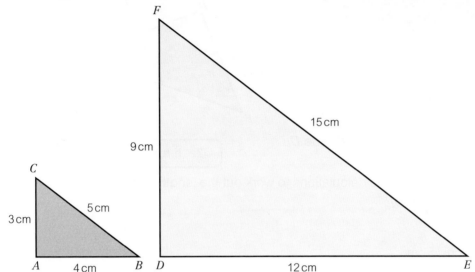

a Copy and complete.
Side *AB* corresponds to side *DE*.
Side *AC* corresponds to side □.
Side □ corresponds to side *EF*.

b i Side *AB* : side *DE* = 4 : □

$$\div 4 \left(\begin{array}{c} 4:12 \\ 1:3 \end{array}\right) \div 4$$

ii Side *AC* : side □ = □ : □

$$\div 3 \left(\begin{array}{c} \square : \square \\ \square : \square \end{array}\right) \div 3$$

> **Q1bii hint** Which side does *AC* correspond to?

iii Side □ : side *EF* = □ : □ = □

$$\div \square \left(\begin{array}{c} \square : \square \\ \square : \square \end{array}\right) \div \square$$

> **Q1biii hint** Which side does *EF* correspond to?

c What do you notice about all the ratios in parts **i**, **ii** and **iii**?

d Copy and complete the statement using the words in the cloud.
If two triangles are _____ the _____ of the lengths of corresponding sides are _____ .

> ratios
> equal
> similar

2 Triangles *ABC* and *DEF* are similar.

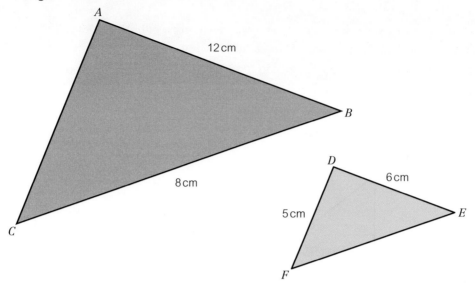

a Work out the ratio of side *AB* : side *DE*.

b Simplify the ratio.

> **Q2a, b hint** Follow the steps in **Q1a** and **b**.

c Copy and complete the calculations to work out the length of side *AC*.

Side *AC* : side *DF*

2 : 1

×☐ (＿＿＿＿＿) ×☐

☐ cm : 5 cm

d Copy and complete the calculations to work out the length of side *EF*.

Side *BC* : side *EF*

2 : 1

×☐ (＿＿＿＿＿) ×☐

8 cm : ☐ cm

3 **Reasoning** May says, 'Triangle *XYZ* and triangle *LMN* are similar because all the sides of triangle *LMN* are 2 cm longer than those in triangle *XYZ*'.

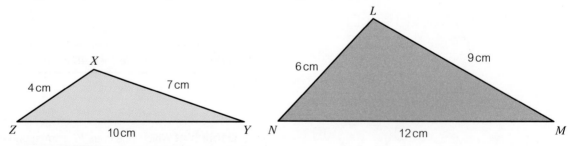

a Work out the ratio of the lengths of sides

  i *XY* to *LM*   **ii** *XZ* to *LN*   **iii** *ZY* to *NM*.

b Simplify the ratios in part **a** if possible.

c Are all the ratios the same?

d Explain why May is wrong.

Angles in similar triangles

1 a Use a protractor to measure the angles in the two triangles in **Q1** on page 132.

   b What do you notice about corresponding angles?

   c Use a protractor to measure the angles in the two triangles in **Q2** on page 133.

   d What do you notice about corresponding angles?

   e Copy and complete.

     In similar triangles, corresponding angles are _____.

2 **Reasoning** Explain why none of these pairs of triangles are similar.

> **Q2 hint** Are corresponding angles equal? Is the ratio between corresponding side lengths the same?

a

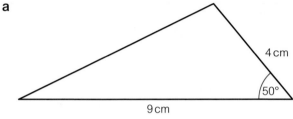 

b

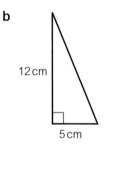 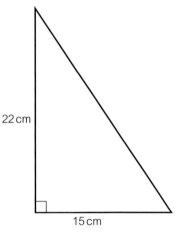

c

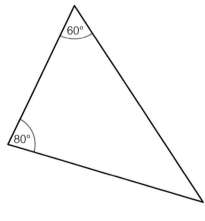 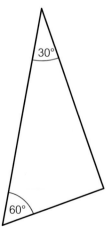

> **Reflect** Write the steps you would use to decide whether two triangles are similar.

10.3 The tangent ratio

- Use conventions for naming the sides of a right-angled triangle
- Work out the tangent ratio of any angle
- Use the tangent ratio to work out an unknown side of a right-angled triangle

Naming the sides of a right-angled triangle

Guided

1 Which side is **opposite** angle θ?

> **Q1 hint** Imagine the angle is an 'eye'. Which side is it looking at?

a

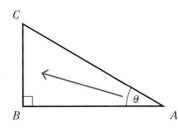

b

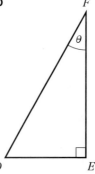

c

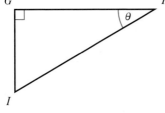

Guided

2 Which side is **adjacent** to angle θ and the right angle?

> **Q2 hint** **Adjacent** means 'next to'.

a

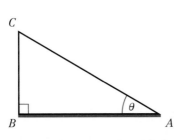

b

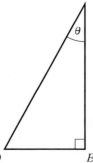

c

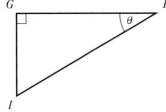

Using the tangent ratio

1 **a** Find the ⟨ tan ⟩ key on your calculator.

    b Type in 'tan 45°' and press the '=' key.

    c Write down your answer.

    d Repeat steps **b–c** to find

       i tan 15°   **ii** tan 30°

       iii tan 60°   **iv** tan 0°

    Round your answers to 1 decimal place, when necessary.

> **Key point** You use the **tangent** ratio to find the length of either the opposite side or the adjacent side in a right-angled triangle. Equivalent ratios between the opposite and adjacent sides always give the same angle.

2 Work out the length of the opposite side of the triangle. Follow the steps below.

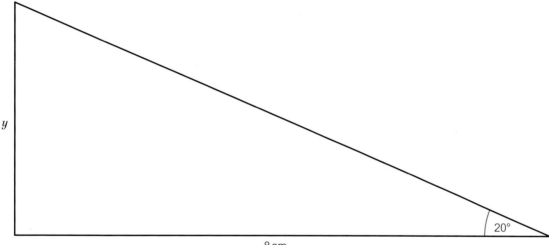

8 cm

    a Copy the tangent ratio: $\tan \theta = \dfrac{\text{opposite}}{\text{adjacent}}$

    b Write down the values you know.

       $\theta = \square$

       opposite $= y$

       adjacent $= \square$ cm

    c Rewrite the tangent ratio, filling in any values you know:

       $\tan \square° = \dfrac{y}{\square}$

    d Rearrange the tangent ratio to give $y = \square$.

    e Use your calculator to work out the value of y.
       Round your answer to 1 decimal place.

> **Q2d hint** $y = \square \times \tan 20°$

> **Q2e hint** Look at the diagram to check your answer makes sense. Will y be more or less than 8 cm?

3 Follow the steps in **Q2** to work out y in each triangle.
Round your answers to 1 decimal place.

Q3 hint y is the opposite side in each triangle.

a

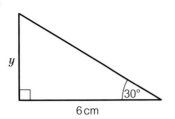

30°
6 cm
y

b

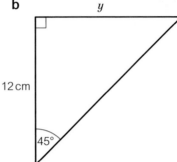

y
12 cm
45°

c

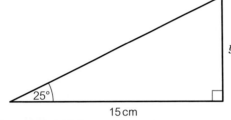

25°
15 cm
y

Worked example

Work out the length of the adjacent side.

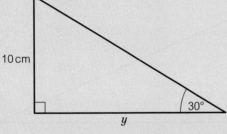

10 cm
30°
y

$\tan \theta = \dfrac{\text{opposite}}{\text{adjacent}}$ —— Write down the tangent ratio.

$\theta = 30°$
opposite $= 10$ —— Write down the values you know.
adjacent $= y$

$\tan 30° = \dfrac{10}{y}$ —— Rewrite the tangent ratio, filling in any values you know.

$y \times \tan 30° = 10$ —— Multiply both sides by y.

$y = \dfrac{10}{\tan 30°}$ —— Divide both sides by $\tan 30°$ to give $y = \square$

$y = 17.3205... = 17.3$ cm —— Use your calculator to work out the value of y.
Round your answer to 1 decimal place.

4 Work out y in each triangle. Round your answers to 1 decimal place.

> **Q4 hint** y is the adjacent side in each triangle.

a

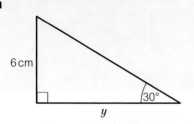

b

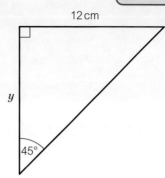

c

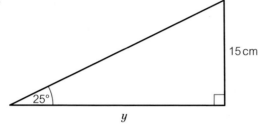

5 **Problem-solving** Match the correct tangent ratio from the box to triangles A and B. Show your working.

$$\tan 30° = \frac{x}{3}$$

$$\tan 30° = \frac{3}{x}$$

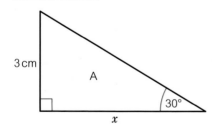

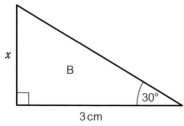

Reflect Draw a right-angled triangle. Mark the right angle. Label one other angle θ. Label the opposite and adjacent sides. Now write down the relationship between $\tan \theta$ and the opposite and adjacent sides.

10.4 The sine ratio

- Work out the sine ratio of any angle
- Use the sine ratio to work out an unknown side of a right-angled triangle

Finding the hypotenuse of a right-angled triangle

1 Which side is the **hypotenuse**?

Q1 hint The **hypotenuse** is the longest side.

a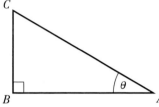

b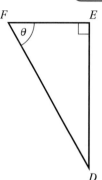

c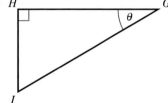

2 Copy and complete these statements using the words in the cloud.
  a The hypotenuse is the _____. It is opposite the _____.
  b The opposite side to angle θ is opposite the _____.
  c The adjacent side to angle θ is _____ θ **and** the _____.

> longest side
> next to
> right angle
> angle θ

Using the sine ratio

 1 **a** Find the sin key on your calculator.
  b Type in 'sin 30°' and press the '=' key.
  c Write down your answer.
  d Repeat steps **b–c** to find
    i sin 15°   **ii** sin 45°   **iii** sin 60°
    iv sin 90°   **v** sin 0°
  Round your answers to 1 decimal place, when necessary.

> **Key point**   You use the **sine** ratio to find the length of either the opposite side or the hypotenuse in a right-angled triangle. Equivalent ratios between the opposite side and hypotenuse always give the same angle.

2 Work out the length of the opposite side of the triangle. Follow the steps below.

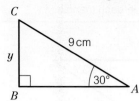

a Write down the sine ratio: $\sin\theta = \dfrac{\text{opposite}}{\text{hypotenuse}}$

b Write down the values you know.

$\theta = \square°$

opposite $= y$

hypotenuse $= \square$

c Rewrite the sine ratio, filling in any values you know: $\sin\square° = \dfrac{y}{\square}$

d Rearrange the sine ratio to give $y = \square$.

e Use your calculator to work out the value of y.
Round your answer to 1 decimal place.

> **Q2d hint**
> $y = \square × \sin 30°$

3 Follow the steps in **Q2** to work out the value of y in each triangle.
Round your answers to 1 decimal place.

> **Q3 hint** y is the opposite side in each triangle.

a

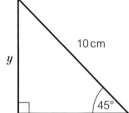

b

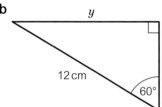

c

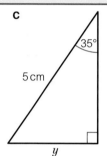

Worked example

Work out the length of the hypotenuse.

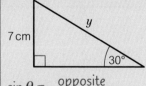

$\sin\theta = \dfrac{\text{opposite}}{\text{hypotenuse}}$ ——— Write down the sine ratio.

$\theta = 30°$

opposite $= 7$

hypotenuse $= y$ ——— Write down the values you know.

$\sin 30° = \dfrac{7}{y}$ ——— Rewrite the sine ratio, filling in any values you know.

$y × \sin 30° = 7$ ——— Rearrange the sine ratio to give $y = \square$. First multiply both sides by y.

$y = \dfrac{7}{\sin 30°}$ ——— Divide both sides by $\sin 30°$.

$y = 14$ cm ——— Use your calculator to work out the length of y.

4 Work out the value of y in each triangle.
Round your answers to 1 decimal place.

Q4 hint y is the hypotenuse in each triangle.

a

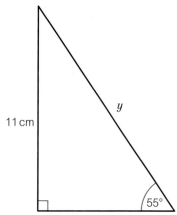

11 cm

y

55°

b

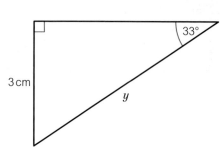

33°

3 cm

y

c

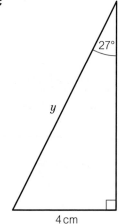

27°

y

4 cm

5 **Problem-solving** Would you use the sine ratio or the tangent ratio to work out the value of y in each of these triangles? Write the correct ratio, filling in any values you know.

Q5 hint Which sides do you know – opposite, adjacent or hypotenuse?

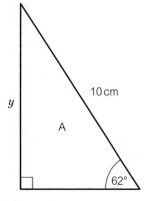

10 cm

y

A

62°

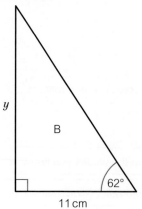

y

B

62°

11 cm

Reflect   What is the same and what is different when using the tangent ratio and the sine ratio?

10.5 The cosine ratio

- Work out the cosine ratio of any angle
- Use the cosine ratio to work out an unknown side of a right-angled triangle

Using the cosine ratio

1 a Find the cos key on your calculator.
   b Type in 'cos 60°' and press the '=' key.
   c Write down your answer.
   d Repeat steps **b–c** to find

      i cos 15°   **ii** cos 30°   **iii** cos 45°

      iv cos 90°   **v** cos 0°

      Round your answers to 1 decimal place, when necessary.

Key point   You use the **cosine** ratio to find the length of either the adjacent side or the hypotenuse in a right-angled triangle. Equivalent ratios between the adjacent side and hypotenuse always give the same angle.

2 Work out the length of the adjacent side of the triangle. Follow the steps below.

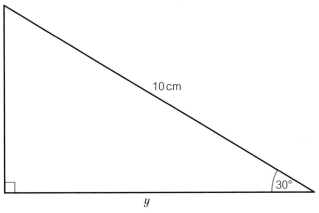

10 cm

30°

y

a Write down the cosine ratio: $\cos \theta = \dfrac{\text{adjacent}}{\text{hypotenuse}}$

b Write down the values you know.

$\theta = \square°$

adjacent = y

hypotenuse = $\square$

c Rewrite the cosine ratio, filling in any values you know: $\cos \square° = \dfrac{y}{\square}$

d Rearrange the cosine ratio to give $y = \square$.

e Use your calculator to work out the value of y.
   Round your answer to 1 decimal place.

Q2d hint
$y = \square \times \cos 30°$

3 Follow the steps in **Q2** to work out y in each triangle. Round your answers to 1 decimal place.

Q3 hint y is the adjacent side in each triangle.

a

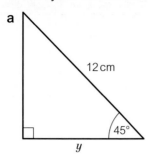

b

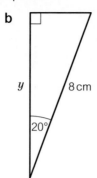

c

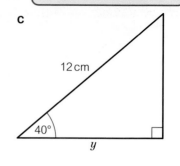

Worked example

Work out the length of the hypotenuse.

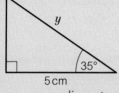

$\cos \theta = \dfrac{\text{adjacent}}{\text{hypotenuse}}$ — Write down the cosine ratio.

$\theta = 35°$

adjacent $= 5$

hypotenuse $= y$ — Write down the values you know.

$\cos 35° = \dfrac{5}{y}$ — Rewrite the cosine ratio, filling in any values you know.

$y \times \cos 35° = 5$ — Rearrange the cosine ratio to give $y = \square$. First multiply both sides by y.

$y = \dfrac{5}{\cos 35°}$ — Divide both sides by $\cos 35°$.

$y = 6.1038... = 6.1\,\text{cm}$ — Use a calculator to work out y. Round the answer to 1 decimal place.

---

4 Work out y in each triangle. Round your answers to 1 decimal place.

Q4 hint y is the hypotenuse in each triangle.

a

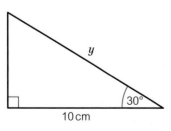

b

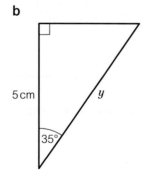

c

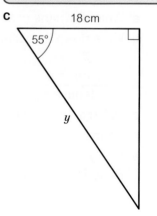

5 Problem-solving Would you use the sine ratio or cosine ratio to find the value of y in these triangles? Write the correct ratio, filling in any values you know.

Q5 hint Which sides do you know – opposite, adjacent or hypotenuse?

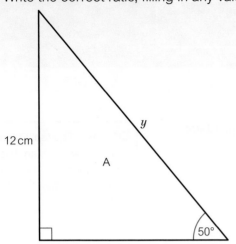

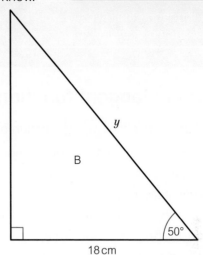

6 Reasoning Antony is working out the value of y in this right-angled triangle.

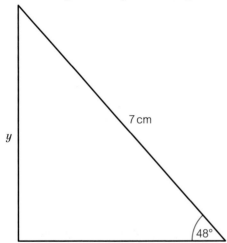

Here is his working.
$\theta = 48°$
adjacent = y
hypotenuse = 7
$\cos \theta = \dfrac{\text{adjacent}}{\text{hypotenuse}}$
What mistake has Antony made?

Reflect Copy and complete the three trigonometric ratios.

$\tan \theta = \dfrac{\square}{\square}$ $\sin \theta = \dfrac{\square}{\square}$ $\cos \theta = \dfrac{\square}{\square}$

Draw a triangle to show when you would use the cosine ratio.

10.6 Using trigonometry to find angles

- Use the trigonometric ratios to work out an unknown angle in a right-angled triangle

The inverse tangent function

1 **a** Find and press the $\boxed{\tan^{-1}}$ function on your calculator.

b Type in the number 1 and press the '=' key.

c Copy and complete: $\tan^{-1}(1) = \Box$

d Repeat steps **b–c** to find

   i $\tan^{-1}(2)$ **ii** $\tan^{-1}(3)$ **iii** $\tan^{-1}(0.5)$

   iv $\tan^{-1}(3.5)$ **v** $\tan^{-1}(5.2)$

Round your answers to 1 decimal place.

> **Q1a hint** The $\tan^{-1}$ function is the **inverse** of tan. It is usually found by pressing $\boxed{\text{SHIFT}}$ and then $\boxed{\tan}$.

2 The lengths of the sides opposite and adjacent to the angle θ are given in the triangle.

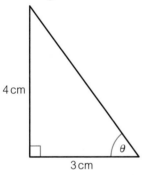

4 cm

3 cm

Follow these steps to work out the size of θ.

a Write down the values you know.

   adjacent = $\Box$ cm

   opposite = $\Box$ cm

b Write down the tangent ratio: $\tan\theta = \dfrac{\text{opposite}}{\text{adjacent}}$

> **Q2b hint** Use the tangent ratio because you know the lengths of the opposite and adjacent sides.

c Rewrite the tangent ratio, filling in any values you know: $\tan\theta = \dfrac{\Box}{\Box}$

d Work out θ by using the '$\tan^{-1}$' function on your calculator. Round your answer to 1 decimal place.

> **Q2d hint** $\tan^{-1}\left(\dfrac{4}{3}\right)$

3 Follow the steps in **Q2** to work out the size of θ in each triangle. Round your answers to 1 decimal place.

> **Q3c hint** Make sure you correctly identify which side is the opposite and which is the adjacent.

a

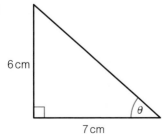

6 cm

7 cm

b

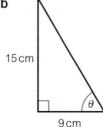

15 cm

9 cm

c

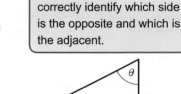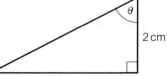

2 cm

4 cm

The inverse sine function

1 a Find and press the $\boxed{\sin^{-1}}$ function on your calculator.

b Type in the number 0.5 and press the '=' key.

c Copy and complete: $\sin^{-1}(0.5) = \square$

d Repeat steps **b–c** to find

   i $\sin^{-1}(0.8)$ **ii** $\sin^{-1}(0.2)$

   iii $\sin^{-1}(0.25)$ **iv** $\sin^{-1}(0.99)$

   v $\sin^{-1}(0.7)$

Round your answers to 1 decimal place.

> **Q1a hint** The $\sin^{-1}$ function is the **inverse** of sin. It is usually found by pressing $\boxed{\text{SHIFT}}$ and then $\boxed{\sin}$.

2 The lengths of the hypotenuse and the side opposite the angle θ are given in the triangle.

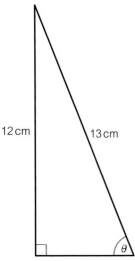

12 cm   13 cm

Follow the steps to work out the size of θ.

a Write down the values you know.

   opposite = $\square$ cm

   hypotenuse = $\square$ cm

b Write down the sine ratio: $\sin\theta = \dfrac{\text{opposite}}{\text{hypotenuse}}$

> **Q2b hint** Use the sine ratio because you know the lengths of the hypotenuse and the opposite side.

c Rewrite the sine ratio, filling in any values you know: $\sin\theta = \dfrac{\square}{\square}$

d Work out θ by using the '$\sin^{-1}$' function on your calculator. Round your answer to 1 decimal place.

> **Q2d hint** $\theta = \sin^{-1}\left(\dfrac{12}{13}\right)$

3 Follow the steps in **Q2** to work out the size of angle θ in each triangle. Round your answers to 1 decimal place.

> **Q3 hint** Make sure you correctly identify which side is the opposite and which is the hypotenuse.

a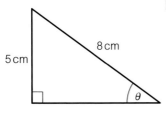

8 cm

5 cm

θ

b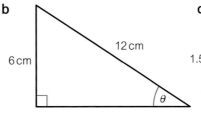

12 cm

6 cm

θ

c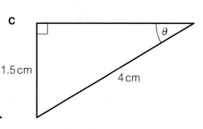

θ

1.5 cm

4 cm

The inverse cosine function

1 **a** Find and press the $\cos^{-1}$ function on your calculator.

b Type in the number 0.5 and press the '=' key.

c Copy and complete: $\cos^{-1}(0.5) = \square$

d Repeat steps **b**–**c** to find

   i $\cos^{-1}(0.8)$ **ii** $\cos^{-1}(0.2)$ **iii** $\cos^{-1}(0.25)$

   iv $\cos^{-1}(0.99)$ **v** $\cos^{-1}(0.7)$

   Round your answers to 1 decimal place.

> **Q1a hint** The $\cos^{-1}$ function is the **inverse** of cos. It is usually found by pressing SHIFT and then cos.

2 The lengths of the hypotenuse and the side adjacent to the angle θ are given in the triangle.

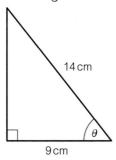

14 cm

9 cm

Follow the steps to work out the size of θ.

a Write down the values you know.

   adjacent = $\square$ cm

   hypotenuse = $\square$ cm

b Write down the cosine ratio: $\cos \theta = \dfrac{\text{adjacent}}{\text{hypotenuse}}$

c Rewrite the cosine ratio, filling in any values you know: $\cos \theta = \dfrac{\square}{\square}$

d Work out θ by using the '$\cos^{-1}$' function on a calculator. Round your answer to 1 decimal place.

> **Q2b hint** Use the cosine ratio because you know the lengths of the hypotenuse and the adjacent side.

> **Q2d hint** $\theta = \cos^{-1}\left(\dfrac{9}{14}\right)$

3 Follow the steps in **Q2** to work out the size of angle θ in each triangle. Round your answers to 1 decimal place.

a

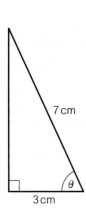

7 cm

3 cm

b

11 cm

4 cm

c

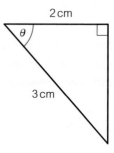

2 cm

3 cm

> **Reflect** Write a list of the new mathematical vocabulary you have used in this lesson. Make sure you spell the words correctly. Write down what they mean.

Answers

UNIT 1 Indices and standard form

1.1 Indices

Priority of operations including negative numbers and powers

1 a 4 b −8 c 16 d −32
2 a True b True c True d True
   e False f True g False h True
3 a 5 b 5 c 3 d −3
   e 21 f 10 g 19
4 No – one gives 5, the other gives −3.

Using the index laws to simplify expressions

1 a $2 \times 2 \times 2$ b $2 \times 2 \times 2 \times 2$
   c 2^7
2 a 3^4 b 3^5 c 3^6
   d 3^7 e 3^8
   f The final power is the sum of the powers being multiplied.
3 a 5^{10} b 5^{15} c 5^4 d 5^8
4 a 3^2 b 3^2 c 3^2

1.2 Calculations and estimates

Estimating powers and roots

1 a 1 b 2 c 3
   d −1 e −2 f −27
2 a 9 b 9 c 10 d 10
3 a 4 b 3 c 6 d 11
4 a i 2 ii 3 iii 1
      iv 5 v 5 vi 2
   b −1, −8, −27, −64, −125
   c i −2 ii −3 iii −1
      iv −5 v −5 vi −2

Estimating calculations

1 a 15 b 10 c 49
   d 50 e 11 f −9
2 a £34 (rounding £8.45 to £8) or £35 (rounding £8.45 to £8.50)
   b If you rounded £8.45 to £8 it will be less.
      If you rounded £8.45 to £8.50 it will be more.

1.3 More indices

More indices

1 a 3^4 b 3^6 c 3^8
2 a 2^6 b 2^8 c 2^{10} d 2^{12}
3 a i 2^3 ii 2^4 iii 2^5
   b i 2^6 ii 2^8 iii 2^{10}
      iv 2^9 v 2^{12} vi 2^{15}
4 a i 3^2 ii 3^3 iii 3^4
   b i 3^6 ii 3^9 iii 3^{12}

Positive and negative powers of 10

1 a

	Millions	Hundred thousands	Ten thousands	Thousands	Hundreds	Tens	Ones	.	$\frac{1}{10}$	$\frac{1}{100}$	$\frac{1}{1000}$
10^6	1	0	0	0	0	0	0	.	0	0	0
10^5		1	0	0	0	0	0	.	0	0	0
10^4			1	0	0	0	0	.	0	0	0
10^3				1	0	0	0	.	0	0	0
10^2					1	0	0	.	0	0	0
10^1						1	0	.	0	0	0
10^0							1	.	0	0	0
10^{-1}							0	.	1	0	0
10^{-2}							0	.	0	1	0
10^{-3}							0	.	0	0	1

   b larger than, smaller than, equal to
   c i $\frac{1}{10}$
      ii 100, $\frac{1}{100}$
      iii 1000, $\frac{1}{1000}$
      iv 10 000, $\frac{1}{10\,000}$
   d i 0.1 ii 0.01
      iii 0.001 iv 0.0001

1.4 Standard form

Multiplying by positive and negative powers of 10

1 a 20
      200
      2000
      20 000
      200 000
   b 3×10
      3×10^2
      3×10^3
      3×10^4
      3×10^5
2 a 0.4 b 0.04 c 0.004
   d 0.5 e 0.05 f 0.005
3 a Yes b Yes

Standard form

1 a 2×10^3 b 6×10^4
   c 9×10^2 d 8×10^4
2 She has written 12 instead of 1.2. The number must be between 1 and 10.
3 a B: 3.4×10^5 b A: 1.23×10^3
   c B: 1.5×10^2 d C 1.4×10^7
4 2×10^{-2}
   2×10^{-3}
   2×10^{-4}
   2×10^{-5}
5 a i 3×10^{-4}
      ii 4×10^{-3}
      iii 5×10^{-2}
      iv 6×10^{-5}
   b 3×10^{-10}
6 a B: 5.3×10^{-5} b B: 1.5×10^{-1}
   c C: 1.05×10^{-2} d B: 1.1×10^{-4}

UNIT 2 Expressions and formulae

2.1 Solving equations

Solving equations involving fractions

1   a $x = 4$ b $y = 25$ c $m = 8$
  d $x = 10$ e $y = 30$ f $m = 8$

Solving equations with fraction solutions

1   a $\frac{1}{2}$ b $\frac{2}{5}$ c $\frac{2}{3}$ d $\frac{5}{2}$

2   a $x = \frac{3}{2}$ b $x = \frac{5}{4}$ c $x = \frac{9}{8}$ d $x = \frac{3}{5}$

3   a $a = 5$ b $x = \frac{7}{2}$ c $m = \frac{10}{3}$
  d $x = \frac{13}{4}$ e $p = \frac{18}{5}$ f $x = \frac{17}{2}$

Solving two-step equations involving fractions

1   a $a = 12$ b $x = 21$ c $p = 64$
2   a $x = 7$ b $x = 2$ c $a = 12$
  d $x = 4$ e $p = 13$ f $m = 11$

Solving equations with unknowns on both sides

1   $x = 7$
2   a $x = 5$ b $x = 4$ c $x = 4$
  d $x = 7$ e $x = 2$ f $x = 8$
3   a $x = 4$ b $x = 5$ c $x = 3$
4   a $x = 4$ b $x = 11$ c $x = 6$
  d $x = 5$ e $x = 13$ f $x = 4$

2.2 Substituting into expressions

Substituting values into expressions involving powers and roots

1   a   9   b   36   c   25
  d   8   e   1   f   64
  g   7   h   5   i   3
2   a   16   b   49   c   0.25
  d   27   e   8
3   a   13   b   5   c   12
  d   6   e   12   f   6
4   a   10   b   6   c   13
  d   3   e   10   f   6
5   a   32   b   3   c   9
  d   11   e   16   f   54
  g   24   h   3   i   14
6   a   18   b   20   c   34
  d   12   e   64   f   32

Substituting values into expressions involving brackets

1   a   36   b   36   c   64   d   9
  e   36   f   25   g   10   h   15
  i   −5   j   36
2   a   121   b   225   c   100   d   4
  e   50   f   52   g   47
3   a   1   b   4   c   7
  d   4   e   6   f   7
4   a   2   b   10
5   a   3   b   6   c   4
6   a   2   b   3
7   a   13   b   6   c   1   d   32
  e   80   f   88   g   21   h   20
8   a   −8   b   −6   c   3   d   9
  e   69   f   27   g   30

2.3 Writing and using formulae

Writing and using formulae

1   a $3a$ b $5b$ c $p + 4$ d $s - 10$
2   a $2n + 4$ b $3(n - 4)$ c $2(n + 3)$ d $2n - 4$
3   $C = 90x$
4   $C = 20 \times g$ or $C = 20g$
5   $C = 50r$
6   a $C = 10 \times t = £10t$ b   £60
7   a $C = 30 \times d + 20$ or $C = 30d + 20$ b   £80

Graphs and formulae

1   a   £30   b   £30
  c   £120   d $C = 30h + 30$

2.4 Using and rearranging formulae

Substituting values, then solving an equation

1   a $T = 13$ b $S = 1$ c $R = 3$
2   a $L = 5$ b $P = 7$
3   a $d = 15$ b $s = 5$ c $t = 3$
4   a $A = 3$ b $F = 24$
5   a   4   b   6.5

Rearranging formulae

1   a $M = 10 - 4$ b $P = 5 + 2$ c $a = \frac{10}{2}$ d $S = 3 \times 5$
2   a $P = S - 2$ b $P = S + 3$ c $P = 2S - 4$ d $P = 3S + 6$
3   a $M = \frac{N}{5}$ b $M = \frac{2N}{3}$ c $M = 2N$ d $M = 8N$
4   a $T = \frac{P}{4}$ b $T = \frac{X}{6}$ c $T = 6Y$
  d $T = Za$ e $T = \frac{Q}{b}$ f $T = \frac{R}{c}$
5   a $P = M - 5$ b $P = M + 4$
  c $P = \frac{M}{6}$ d $P = 5M$
6   a $S = T - R$ b $S = T + R$
  c $S = \frac{T}{R}$ d $S = RT$
7   a $x = \frac{y - c}{2}$ b $x = \frac{y + c}{2}$
  c $x = \frac{3y - 4c}{2}$ d $x = \frac{3y + 5c}{2}$

2.5 Index laws and brackets

Rules of indices

1   a 2^7 b 3^5 c 5^5
  d 7^6 e a^{10} f y^6
  g   You add the powers to get the answer.
2   a $6a^5$ b $8a^7$ c $12b^7$
  d $10x^6$ e $20c^5$
3   a 4^2 b 5^3 c 3^3
  d 6^2 e t^3 f s^2
  g   You subtract the powers to get the answer.
4   a $5b^3$ b $4b^3$ c $3x^2$
  d $4a^6$ e $10y^2$
5   a 3^8 b 5^6 c a^{12}
  d x^{12} e $16m^6$ f $27p^{15}$
6   8, 4, 2, 1
7   a   10   b   1   c   16
  d   1   e   3   f   1

Collecting like terms involving powers

1   a $2a$ b $2a^2$ c $2a^3$
  d $3b^2$ e $4x^2$
2   a $7a$ b $7a^2$ c $5a^3$
  d $6b^2$ e $6b^2$

Expanding brackets: grid method

1   a $3x + 6$ b $4y + 20$ c $4x + 6$ d $20a - 15$
2   $y^2 + y$
3   a $x^2 + x$ b $y^2 - 3y$ c $2a^2 + 4a$ d $4p^2 - 3p$
4   $p^3 + 4p$
5   a $p^3 + 2p$ b $x^3 + 3x$ c $a^3 - 3a$ d $y^3 - y$

Factorising by taking out one term

1   a   4   b   10
2   a $2(2x + 3)$ b $2(4a + 1)$ c $4(3b + 1)$ d $10(2y + 1)$
3   a $x(x + 2)$ b $y(y + 3)$ c $a(a - 5)$
  d $p(p - 10)$ e $2x(x + 2)$ f $3b(b + 2)$

2.6 Expanding double brackets

Expanding double brackets

1   966
2   735

3 $a^2 + 7a + 10$

4 a $x^2 + 7x + 12$ **b** $a^2 + 3a + 2$
  c $a^2 + 8a + 15$ **d** $y^2 + 6y + 8$

5 a $x^2 + 2x - 8$ **b** $x^2 - 2x - 8$
  c $x^2 - 6x + 8$
  d They are the same apart from the number in front of the x, which is negative in **b**.

6 a $a^2 + a - 20$ **b** $p^2 - p - 6$
  c $m^2 - 6m + 8$

7 a $x^2 + 8x + 16$ **b** $y^2 + 4y + 4$
  c $p^2 - 2p + 1$

UNIT 3 Dealing with data

3.1 Planning a survey

Choosing which data to collect

1   a   B
    b   D

2   Age (A) and salary (C)

3   Gender (B) and salary (C)

Primary and secondary data

1   Hannah and Tim

2   Lamarr and Olivia

3   Hannah, Tim, Ethan and Ruth

4   Ryan, Sasha, Lamarr and Olivia

Sample size

1   a   50   b   200   c   25   d   8

2   a   50   b   200   c   25   d   8

Data collection

1   a   i   C   ii   D   iii   A   iv   B
    b   A and D

2   i   B   ii   C   iii   A

Bias and random samples

1   a   Danny is only asking people in his family.
    b   Yes, Danny's family is not a representative
        sample of the town.

2   a   Usman might arrive early to school. The first 10 people he
        sees would also be early and they might be happier to start
        school earlier.
    b   Becky's friends might share the same taste in
        restaurants as she does.
    c   People who are shopping in a town centre might be more
        inclined to say they want more parking.

3.2 Collecting data

Discrete and continuous data

1   a   No, it is not possible to receive 0.3 of an email.
    b   Yes, the data is discrete. The amount of emails can only
        take whole-number values.

2   The data is continuous, because the lengths can take any value
    in a range. If the measuring instrument was more accurate, the
    lengths could be given to 3 or more decimal places.

3   Discrete. Each value must be a whole number because you are
    counting people.

Data collection sheets

1   a

Portions of fruit	Portions of fruit (grouped)	Tally	Frequency
0, 1, 2, 3, 4, 5	0–5	|||	3
6, 7, 8, 9, 10, 11	6–11	||	2
12, 13, 14, 15, 16, 17	12–17	||||	4
18, 19, 20, 21, 22, 23	18–23	||	2

    b   Discrete

2   a

Reaction times	Tally	Frequency
$0.0 \leqslant x < 0.2$	||	2
$0.2 \leqslant x < 0.4$			1
$0.4 \leqslant x < 0.6$	||||	4
$0.6 \leqslant x < 0.8$	|||	3

    b   Continuous

3   a   Discrete
    b   1
    c   22
    d   0 and 24 or 25

e

Days exercised	Tally	Frequency
0–4	||	2
5–9	|||||	5
10–14	|||	3
15–19	|||	3
20–24			1

4   a   Continuous
    b   5.8
    c   8.5
    d   5 and 9

e

Length of finger (cm)	Tally	Frequency
$5 \leqslant x < 6$			1
$6 \leqslant x < 7$	|||	3
$7 \leqslant x < 8$	|||	3
$8 \leqslant x < 9$	|||	3

Two-way tables

1   a   20–29, 30–39
    b   Blue, Brown, Green
    c

		Eye colour		
		Blue	Brown	Green
Age	20–29			
	30–39			

2   a   Year 9, Year 10
    b $150 \leqslant x < 160$, $160 \leqslant x < 170$
    c

		Year group	
		9	10
Height (cm)	$150 \leqslant x < 160$		
	$160 \leqslant x < 170$		

Designing a questionnaire

1   a   Question A is encouraging you to pick 'Yes'.
    b   Thomas should use question B because it is not a
        leading question.

2   Question A has the better response section because there are
    no missing values.

3   a   Question B. People will interpret 'too much' homework in
        different ways.
    b   Amir should use question A.

3.3 Calculating averages

Calculating the median from a table

1   a   0, 0, 0, 0, 0, 0, | 1, 1, 1, 1, 1, 1, 1, 1, | 2, 2, 2, | 3, 3

        6 people have 0 siblings   8 people have 1 sibling   3 people have 2 siblings   2 people have 3 siblings

    b   10th value

    c   0, 0, 0, 0, 0, 0, | 1, 1, 1, (1), 1, 1, 1, 1, | 2, 2, 2, | 3, 3

        6 people have 0 siblings   8 people have 1 sibling   3 people have 2 siblings   2 people have 3 siblings

    d   1 sibling

2   a

Number of computers	Frequency	Running total
0	5	5
1	7	5 + 7 = 12
2	14	12 + 14 = 26
3	2	26 + 2 = 28
4	1	28 + 1 = 29
Total	29	

    b   15th value

c i Houses 1–5 have 0 computers.
  ii Houses 6–12 have 1 computer.
  iii Houses 13–26 have 2 computers.
  iv Houses 27–28 have 3 computers.
  v House 29 has 4 computers.
d 2 computers

Calculating the mean from a grouped frequency table

1 a 15   b 7.5   c 20
  d 28   e 13   f 25.5

2

Time taken, t (seconds)	Frequency	Midpoint of class
$0 \leqslant t < 20$	3	$\frac{0+20}{2} = \frac{20}{2} = 10$
$20 \leqslant t < 40$	15	30
$40 \leqslant t < 60$	8	50
$60 \leqslant t < 80$	4	70
Total	30	

3 a–c

Books, b	Frequency	Midpoint of class	Midpoint × frequency
$0 \leqslant b < 4$	6	$\frac{0+4}{2} = \frac{4}{2} = 2$	$2 \times 6 = 12$
$4 \leqslant b < 8$	4	$\frac{4+8}{2} = \frac{12}{2} = 6$	$6 \times 4 = 24$
$8 \leqslant b < 12$	11	10	$10 \times 11 = 110$
$12 \leqslant b < 16$	3	14	$14 \times 3 = 42$
$16 \leqslant b < 20$	1	18	$18 \times 1 = 18$
Total	25		206

d 206 books

4 a

Bath time, t (minutes)	Frequency	Midpoint of class	Midpoint × frequency
$0 \leqslant t < 5$	8	$\frac{0+5}{2} = \frac{5}{2} = 2.5$	$2.5 \times 8 = 20$
$5 \leqslant t < 10$	5	7.5	37.5
$10 \leqslant t < 15$	13	12.5	162.5
$15 \leqslant t < 20$	4	17.5	70
Total	30		290

b 290 minutes
c An estimate for the mean time spent in the bath is $\frac{290}{30} = 9.67$ minutes.

5 a

Letters, l	Frequency	Midpoint of class	Midpoint × frequency
0–2	1	1	$1 \times 1 = 1$
3–5	14	4	$4 \times 14 = 56$
6–8	8	7	$7 \times 8 = 56$
9–11	2	10	$10 \times 2 = 20$
Total	25		133

b 133 letters
c An estimate for the mean number of letters in people's first names is $\frac{133}{25} = 5.32$

6 a $\frac{206}{25} = 8.24$ books
  b It is an estimate because you have used midpoints of the groups to work it out instead of exact numbers.

3.4 Displaying and analysing data

Outliers and correlation

1 Graphs B and D
2 Graphs A, D and E – positive correlation
  Graphs B and C – negative correlation

Using lines of best fit to estimate

1 a 9 hours
  b 7 years old
2 a Line 2
  b Line 1
  c Line 1

3 a £116
  b 63 minutes

Further enquiry

1 a 10% of 600 = 60
  b They might spend very different amounts of time watching TV on different days.
  c Ask more students – at least 10%. Ask about different days of the week.

Drawing a line graph to represent grouped data

1 a Graph axes copied correctly
  b (2, 6), (6, 4), (10, 11), (14, 3), (18, 1)
  c and d

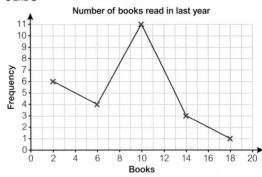

Number of books read in last year

2 a 3 pm
  b 12.30 pm
  c 12 pm
  d 2.30 pm

3 a

Time	Frequency	Midpoint of class
12 pm–1 pm	3	12.30 pm
1 pm–2 pm	7	1.30 pm
2 pm–3 pm	9	2.30 pm
3 pm–4 pm	8	3.30 pm
4 pm–5 pm	4	4.30 pm

b

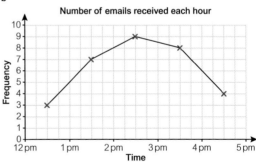

Number of emails received each hour

3.5 Presenting and comparing data

Interpreting charts

1 a In 2015/16 team A won 11 matches.
  b In 2014/15 team B won more matches than team A.
  c In 2018/19 team A won 24 matches.
  d Look at other seasons before 2014/15.
  e Look at the other teams in the league.

Stem and leaf diagrams

1 a 6, 12, 21, 28, 33, 43
  b i 8th value, 21
    ii 6
    iii 42
    iv 36
  c i 28
    ii 12
    iii 43
    iv 31

2 a

```
    Pictures   |   |  Words
        8 6 | 0 | 7 9
        □ 3 0 | 1 | 0 0 2 5 7 7 8
      □□□□□ | 2 | 2 8
          □ | 3 |
```

| Key 3 | 1 means 13   1 | 0 means 10 |

b i The range of words remembered is 28 − 7 = 21
   ii The median number of words remembered is 15.

c

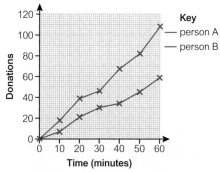

```
    Pictures   |   |  Words
        8 6 | 0 | 7 9
      4 3 0 | 1 | 0 0 2 5 7 8 8
  8 6 6 2 0 | 2 | 2 8
          0 | 3 |
```

| Key 3 | 1 means 13   1 | 0 means 10 |

d i 22
   ii 20

Writing a report

1 a

Number of donations received

[Line graph: y-axis "Donations" from 0 to 120 in steps of 20; x-axis "Time (minutes)" from 0 to 60 in steps of 10. Two lines labelled in Key: person A and person B. Person A rises from 0 to about 108; person B rises from 0 to about 58.]

Key
— person A
— person B

b The results show that person A collected more donations than person B.

c These results support Lakshmi's hypothesis.

d Lakshmi could improve this study by collecting data for a longer time period, collecting data on different days or investigating more/additional locations.

UNIT 4 Multiplicative reasoning

4.1 Enlargement

Enlarging a shape by a scale factor about a centre of enlargement

1 a i 3   **ii** 3   **iii** 3

  b If you enlarge a shape by a scale factor of 3 the sides will all be 3 times longer.

  c i 4 down and 12 down   **ii** 8 down and 24 down

    iii 2 across 8 down and 6 across 24 down

  d To enlarge a shape by a scale factor of 3, make each vertex of the enlarged shape 3 times the distance from the centre of enlargement.

2 a Shape copied onto squared paper

  b i ✕ to A   2 squares across right

    ii ✕ to B   6 squares across right

    iii ✕ to C   6 squares across right, 3 squares down

    iv ✕ to D   2 squares across right, 3 squares down

  c i ✕ to A'   2 × 2 = 4 squares across right

    ii ✕ to B'   6 × 2 = 12 squares across right

    iii ✕ to C'   6 × 2 = 12 squares across right, 3 × 2 = 6 squares down

    iv ✕ to D'   2 × 2 = 4 squares across right, 3 × 2 = 6 squares down

  d

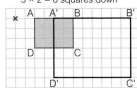

  e Students check the lengths.

3 a Shape copied onto squared paper.

  b

For ABC	
Vertex	Distance from ✕
A	2 right
B	2 right, 3 down
C	6 right, 3 down

For A'B'C'	
Vertex	Distance from ✕
A'	2 × 3 = 6 right
B'	2 × 3 = 6 right 3 × 3 = 9 down
C'	6 × 3 = 18 right 3 × 3 = 9 down

  c

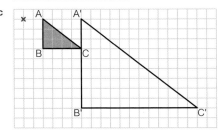

  d Students check the lengths.

4 a The sides of the enlarged shape are not all twice as long as the corresponding sides of the original shape.

  b B' and C'

  c and d

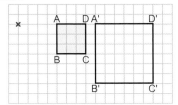

Finding the scale factor and centre of enlargement

1 a 1   **b** 3   **c** 3   **d** 3

  e Students check the lengths.

2 a Shapes copied onto squared paper   **b** 2

  c–f

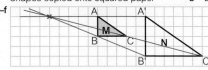

3 a i 3   **ii** 2

  b i

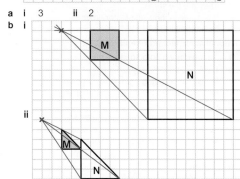

    ii

4.2 Negative and fractional scale factors

Negative scale factors of enlargement

1 a i A   1 square right, 1 square up

    ii B   3 squares right, 1 square up

    iii C   1 square right, 5 squares up

  b i A'   2 squares left, 2 squares down

    ii B'   6 squares left, 2 squares down

    iii C'   2 squares left, 10 squares down

  c

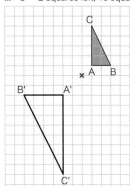

2 a -

  b

For original shape	
Vertex	Distance from ✕
A	2 right, 1 up
B	6 right, 1 up
C	6 right, 2 down
D	2 right, 2 down

For enlargement	
Vertex	Distance from ✕
A'	2 × 1 = 2 left 1 × 1 = 1 down
B'	6 × 1 = 6 left 1 × 1 = 1 down
C'	6 × 1 = 6 left 2 × 1 = 2 up
D'	2 × 1 = 2 left 2 × 1 = 2 up

c

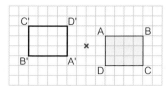

3　**a**　2 times
　　b　It is equal to the scale factor / it has the same magnitude.
　　c　They are the same.
　　d　It is equal to the scale factor times −1 /
　　　　the magnitude of −1 is 1.

Fractional scale factors of enlargement

1　**a**　Shape copied onto squared paper
　　b　**i**　A　8 squares right, 6 squares up
　　　　ii　B　14 squares right, 6 squares up
　　　　iii　C　14 squares right, 2 squares up
　　　　iv　D　8 squares right, 2 squares up
　　c　**i**　A'　4 squares right, 3 squares up
　　　　ii　B'　7 squares right, 3 squares up
　　　　iii　C'　7 squares right, 1 square up
　　　　iv　D'　4 squares right, 1 square up
　　d

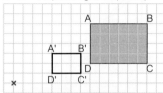

2　**a**　Shape copied onto squared paper.
　　b

For original shape ABC	
Vertex	Distance from ×
A	6 right
B	6 right, 6 down
C	9 right, 6 down

For enlargement A'B'C'	
Vertex	Distance from ×
A'	$6 \times \frac{1}{3} = 2$ right
B'	$6 \times \frac{1}{3} = 2$ right
	$6 \times \frac{1}{3} = 2$ down
C'	$9 \times \frac{1}{3} = 3$ right
	$6 \times \frac{1}{3} = 2$ down

　　c

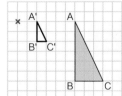

4.3 Percentage change

Finding the original value

1　**a**　£262.50
　　b　£400
2　**a**　Shirt = £27　Tie = £9.45　Shoes = £108
　　b　**i**　£81　**ii**　£198　**iii**　£130.50
　　c　**i**　£36　**ii**　£45　**iii**　£100
3　**a**　80%　　**b**　£25 000 ÷ 0.8 = £31 250
4　**a**　It is smaller than £17 000
　　b　She has multiplied by 0.85 instead of dividing.
　　c　£20 000

Calculating percentage change

1　**a**　£100　　**b**　20%
2　**a**　9 minutes
　　b　45 minutes
　　c　$\frac{9}{45} \times 100 = 20\%$
3　**a**　He has divided by the new price instead of the original price.
　　b　19%

4.4 Compound measures

Speed, distance and time

1　**a**　12.5 km/h　**b**　40 mph　**c**　2 cm/min
2　**a**　Distance = speed × time
　　b　210 miles
3　**a**　20 miles
　　b　**i**　2 hours　**ii**　5 hours　**iii**　1.5 hours
4　**a**　60 miles　**b**　80 miles　**c**　50 miles
5　**a**　600 m　**b**　36 000 m　**c**　36 km
　　d　36 km/h
　　e　A sprinter would not be able to keep running at this
　　　　speed for an hour.
6　**a**　14.4 km/h　**b**　720 km/h　**c**　126 km/h
7　**a**　14 m/s　**b**　33 m/s　**c**　22 m/s

Density, mass and volume

1　**a**　10 g/cm³　**b**　20 g/cm³　**c**　8 g/cm³
2　**a**　2.4 g　**b**　12 g　**c**　4.2 g
3　**a**　2 cm³　**b**　0.5 cm³　**c**　0.33 cm³

Pressure, force and area

1　**a**　1 N/cm²　**b** 0.25 N/cm²　**c**　25 N/cm²
2　**a**　400 N　**b** 2400 N　**c**　100 N
3　**a**　4 cm²　**b** 11 cm²　**c**　0.5 cm²

4.5 Direct and inverse proportion

Direct proportion

1　**a**　£9.10
　　b　£4.20
　　c　£4.90
　　d　Dividing by 2 is the same as multiplying by $\frac{1}{2}$; the cost of a
　　　　5-mile journey will be half of the cost of a 10-mile journey.
2　**a**　£0.45　　**b**　£0.90
　　c　£2.25　　**d**　£1.35
　　e　Find $\frac{1}{2}$ of £2.70
3　In both types of pack, 1 bag costs 35p so neither is better
　value for money.
4　**a**　**i**　30p　**ii**　40p
　　b　Large

Inverse proportion

1　**a**　Less time
　　b　**i**　3 hours　**ii**　2 hours　**iii**　1 hour
2　**a**　$\frac{1}{2}$ hour　**b**　20 minutes
3　12 hours
4　**a**　4 hours　**b**　8 hours　**c**　1 hour

UNIT 5 Constructions

5.1 Using scales

Reading scale drawings

1
cm	0	1	2	3	4	5	6	7	8	9	10	11	12
m	0	4	8	12	16	20	24	28	32	36	40	44	48

2 **a** 10 km **b** 20 km **c** 16 km **d** 50 km

3 **a** 2 cm **b** 4 cm **c** 5 cm **d** 10 cm

4 **a** **i** 4 cm **ii** 2.5 cm **iii** 3.5 cm
   b **i** 200 m **ii** 125 m **iii** 175 m
   c 300 m

Drawing diagrams to scale

1 **a** **i** 9 cm
      ii 6 cm
      iii 1.5 cm
      iv 4.5 cm
      v 7 cm
      vi 2 cm

   b **i**

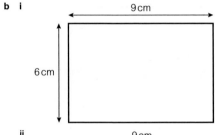

   ii

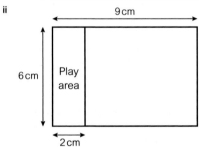

   iii

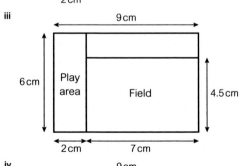

   iv

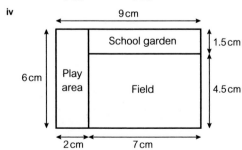

Using scales given as ratios

1 **a** 1 m **b** 10 m **c** 100 m

2 **a** 1 cm on the map represents 10 000 cm in real life.
   b 100 m
   c 1 cm on the map represents 100 m in real life.
   d **i** 400 m **ii** 500 m **iii** 1000 m **iv** 2000 m

3 **a** 2 m **b** 20 m **c** 200 m **d** 2000 m

4 **a** 1 cm on the map represents 20 000 cm in real life.
   b 200 m
   c 1 cm on the map represents 200 m in real life.
   d **i** 800 m **ii** 1000 m **iii** 2000 m **iv** 4000 m
   e **i** 0.8 km **ii** 1 km **iii** 2 km **iv** 4 km

5 **a** 1 cm on the map represents 2500 cm in real life = 25 m.
   b 100 m
   c 16 cm

5.2 Basic constructions

Drawing a circle

1 **a–e** Student draws and labels a circle of radius 6 cm.

2 Student draws a circle of radius 9 cm.

Constructing a perpendicular bisector

1 **a** No **b** Yes **c** No **d** Yes

2 **a** **i** No **ii** Yes **iii** Yes **iv** No
   b The line in **ii**

3 **a**

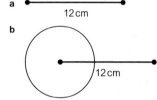

   b

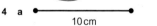

4 **a**

   10 cm

   b

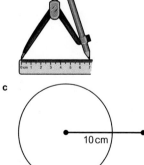

   c

5 **a**

   10 cm

   b

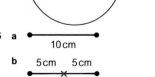

   c

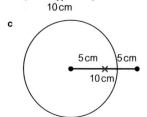

Answers 156

6 a

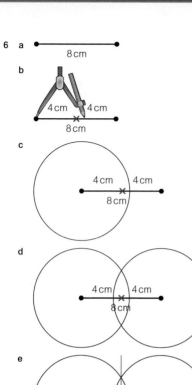

b

c

d

e

7 a 90°
   b 4 cm, 4 cm
   c Perpendicular because the angle is 90°. Bisector because the line is cut in half.

Constructing an angle bisector

1 a Yes   **b** No   **c** No   **d** Yes

2 a

b

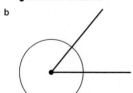

c

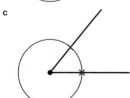

d

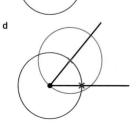

e

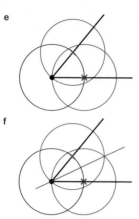

f

Constructing a perpendicular from a point to a line

1 a

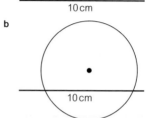

b

c

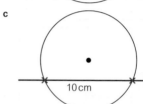

d

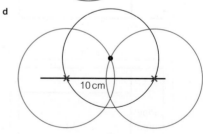

e

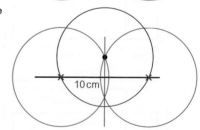

5.3 Constructing triangles

Constructing a triangle when you know the side lengths

1 a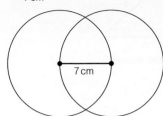
7 cm

b

7 cm

c

7 cm

d 7 cm, 7 cm, 7 cm
e An equilateral triangle

2 a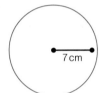
7 cm

b

7 cm

c

7 cm

d

7 cm

e 7 cm, 8 cm, 9 cm

3 a
6 cm

b

6 cm

c

6 cm

d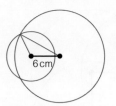

6 cm

e Student prediction. Correct answers are 6 cm, 5 cm, 9 cm.
f 6 cm, 5 cm, 9 cm

Constructing a right-angled triangle

1 a
8 cm

b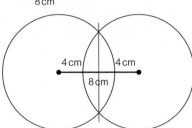
4 cm   4 cm
8 cm

c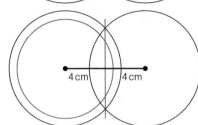
4 cm   4 cm

d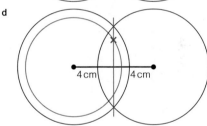
4 cm   4 cm

e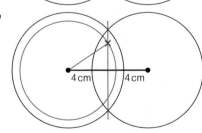
4 cm   4 cm

Constructing a net of a solid

1 a
5 cm
5 cm

b

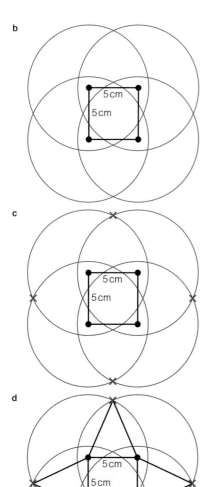

c

d

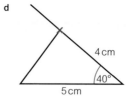

4 cm

40°

5 cm

Constructing a scale diagram

1 a i 10 cm
  ii 4 cm
  b

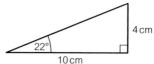

4 cm

22°

10 cm

  c Approximately 10.8 cm
  d Approximately 10.8 m
2 a 6 cm
  b 15°
  c A 6 cm vertical line drawn.
  d i A 90° angle drawn at the bottom of the line.
    ii A 15° angle drawn at the top of the line.
  e Approximately 6.2 cm
  f Approximately 12.4 m

Distance from a point to a line

1 a i 3 cm
  ii 3.7 cm
  iii line 1
  b i 3.7 cm
  ii Approximately 3.8 cm
  iii line 1
  c i Approximately 3.8 cm
  ii 3.7 cm
  iii line 2
  d They are the lines at right angles to the unlabelled line in each diagram.
2 a i 4 cm
  ii 8 cm
  iii 7 cm
  b

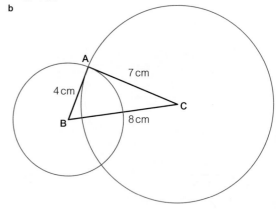

5.4 Using accurate scale diagrams

Drawing a triangle accurately

1 a A 40° angle drawn accurately.
  b A 110° angle drawn accurately.
  c A 65° angle drawn accurately.
  d A 135° angle drawn accurately.
2 a
  ───────────
  5 cm
  b

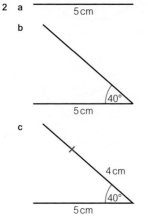

5 cm

  c

4 cm

40°

5 cm

c   i

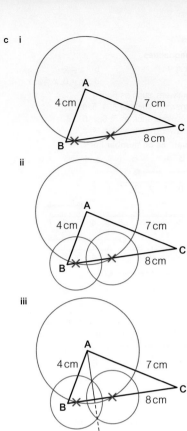

ii

iii

d   Approximately 3.5 cm
e   Approximately 14.0 km

UNIT 6 Sequences, inequalities, equations and proportion

6.1 nth term of arithmetic sequences

Using the nth term

1. **a** 40, 50 **b** 6, 7
   c 5, 7, 9, 11 **d** 5, 8, 11, 14
2. **a** 2, 4, 6, 8, 10 **b** 6, 7, 8, 9, 10
   c 5, 7, 9, 11, 13
3. **a** 12 **b** 7 **c** 10 **d** 21
4. **a** 1 and 5 **b** 25 and 41 **c** 45 and 77
5. **a** -7 **b** -1 **c** -3
6. 3, 10, 17, 24, 31
7. **a** -6 **b** -1 **c** -16
8. **a** 8, 9, 10, 11, 12 **b** 4, 8, 12, 16, 20
   c 4, 9, 14, 19, 24
9. $5n$: 5, 10, 15, 20, 25
   $n + 5$: 6, 7, 8, 9, 10
   $3n + 1$: 4, 7, 10, 13, 16
   $n + 3$: 4, 5, 6, 7, 8
   $3n - 1$: 2, 5, 8, 11, 14

Finding the nth term

1. **a** **i** add 3 **ii** add 5 **iii** add 7
   b The coefficient of n in the nth term is the same as the number added in the term-to-term rule.
   c $2n$
2. **a** iii **b** i **c** ii
3. **a** $3n + 2$ **b** $3n - 2$ **c** $3n - 1$
4. **a** $4n + 2$ **b** $2n + 5$ **c** $3n + 1$
   d $5n - 4$ **e** $3n + 10$
5. **a** **i** $3n + 3$ **ii** 33
   b **i** $5n - 3$ **ii** 47
   c **i** $2n + 13$ **ii** 33
6. **a** $-2n + 12$ **b** $-3n + 17$ **c** $-n + 21$
   d $-3n$ **e** $-4n$
7. **a** $-4n - 3$ **b** -83
8. **a** $2n + 1$ **b** 21
9. **a** 2, 5, 8 **b** 15

6.2 Non-linear sequences

Geometric sequences

1. **a** **i** ×3 **ii** 54
   b **i** ×4 **ii** 64
   c **i** ×3 **ii** 27
   d **i** ×10 **ii** 2000
2. **a** 300, 3000 **b** 24, 48 **c** 36, 108
3. **a** 2.5 **b** 1.5 **c** 0.5 **d** 1.5
4. **a** ×1.5; 4.5, 6.75 **b** ×0.5; 12, 6
   c ×0.4 or $×\frac{2}{5}$; 3.2, 1.28
5. **a** **i** G **ii** A
   b **i** A **ii** G
   c **i** A **ii** G
6. **a** Yes **b** No **c** No
7. **a** ×2 **b** £8 **c** £31

Quadratic sequences

1. **a** A 4-by-4 square, 16 **b** Square numbers
   c 25, 36, 49, 64 **d** +7, +9, +11
2. **a** +9 **b** Going up by 2
   c +2 **d** 38
3. **a** 1st differences: +1, +2, +3, +4; 2nd difference: +1
   b 23, 29
4. 3, 12, 27, 48, 75
5. **a** 2, 8, 18, 32, 50 **b** 2, 5, 10, 17, 26
   c 5, 14, 29, 50, 77
6. Geometric: 162, quadratic: 100, so the geometric sequence has the larger 5th term.

6.3 Inequalities

Interpreting inequalities

1. **a** $x = 6, x = 9$ **b** $x = 2$
   c $x = 6$ **d** $x = 0, x = 2, x = 4$
2. **a** Many answers, such as 6, 5, 4, 3, …
   b Many answers, such as 3, 4, 5, 6, …
   c Many answers, such as 5, 6, 7, 8, …
   d Many answers, such as 6, 5, 4, 3, …

Showing inequalities on number lines

1. **a** iv **b** ii **c** i **d** iii **e** v
2. **a**
   b
   c
   d
3. **a** $x > 2$ **b** $x \geqslant 1$ **c** $x > -2$ **d** $x \leqslant 5$
4. **a** $-2 < x \leqslant 3$ **b** $-2 \leqslant x \leqslant 4$
   c $-3 < x < 1$ **d** $-2 \leqslant x < 5$
5. **a**
   b
   c
   d
6. **a** ii **b** i **c** iv **d** iii
7. **a** $-1, 0, 1, 2, 3, 4$ **b** $-3, -2, -1, 0, 1, 2$
   c 1, 2, 3 **d** 1, 2, 3, 4
8. **a**
   b $7 < x \leqslant 14$
   c 8, 9, 10, 11, 12, 13, 14
9. $12 \leqslant x \leqslant 19$

6.4 Solving equations

Solving equations with fractions

1. **a** $(x + 2) \div 7 = 4$ **b** $(x - 1) \div 8 = 6$
   c $1 = (x - 12) \div 4$
2. **a** $x \rightarrow \boxed{-3} \rightarrow \boxed{\div 15} \rightarrow 1$
   b $a \rightarrow \boxed{+2} \rightarrow \boxed{\div 3} \rightarrow 2$
   c $y \rightarrow \boxed{+7} \rightarrow \boxed{\div 4} \rightarrow 9$
   d $d \rightarrow \boxed{-10} \rightarrow \boxed{\div 2} \rightarrow 20$
3. **a** $x = 11$ **b** $y = 7$ **c** $x = 16$
4. **a** $a = 32$ **b** $b = 37$ **c** $c = 18$ **d** $d = 23$
   e $e = 18$ **f** $f = 3$
5. **a** $\frac{n - 3}{4}$ **b** $\frac{n - 3}{4} = 7$ **c** 31

Solving equations with powers

1. **a** $x = 5, x = -5$ **b** $x = 3, x = -3$
   c $x = 10, x = -10$ **d** $x = 8, x = -8$
   e $x = 6, x = -6$
2. **a** $x = 4, x = -4$ **b** $x = 5, x = -5$
   c $x = 6, x = -6$ **d** $a = 10, a = -10$
   e $e = 8, e = -8$ **f** $b = 3, b = -3$
3. **a** $x = 3.6$ **b** $x = 4.8$
   c $x = 2.8$

4 **a** x^2 **b** $x^2 = 49$
  c $x = 7$ **d** A length cannot be negative.

6.5 Proportion

Writing formulae for direct proportion

1 **a** 3   **b** (0, 0)   **c** $y = 3x$

2 **a** Yes   **b** No   **c** Yes

3 **a** When one variable doubles, the other doubles.
  b $d = kt$
  c $d = 0.5t$
  d $d = 0.5\,\text{km}$ or $500\,\text{m}$

4 **a** 16.5 g, 30 cm, 33 g, 60 cm   **b** Yes
  c $e = 1.25m$

5 **a** 140p
  b $c = 14n$
  c 420p or £4.20

6 **a** $y = 10x$ **b** $y = 70$

Writing formulae for inverse proportion

1 **a** Yes   **b** No   **c** Yes

2 **a** 2 days   **b** $n = \dfrac{2}{t}$ **c** 4 people

3 **a** $y = \dfrac{12}{x}$ **b** $y = 2$

UNIT 7 Circles, Pythagoras and prisms

7.1 Circumference of a circle

Parts of a circle

1 a–e

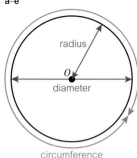

```
        radius
          O
        diameter

      circumference
```

2 a True
  b False
  c True
  d True
  e True
3 a Diameter = 12 cm
    Radius = 6 cm
  b Diameter = 22 cm
    Radius = 11 cm
  c Radius = 9 cm
    Diameter = 18 cm
  d Radius = 7 cm
    Diameter = 14 cm

Calculating the circumference of a circle

1 a 3.14
  b i 6.3   ii 9.4   iii 12.6   iv 15.7
2 a 25.1 cm   b 34.6 cm
  c 18.8 cm   d 3.1 cm
3 Aisha worked out the diameter first, Olivia multiplied πr by 2.
4 a 63 cm
  b 68 cm
  c 70 cm
  d £1.40

7.2 Area of a circle

Area of a circle

1 a 153.9 cm²   b 254.5 cm²
  c 3.1 m²   d 78.5 cm²
  e 706.9 mm²   f 0.8 m²
2 a 12 m²
  b 12.6 m²
  c Smaller, 3 is smaller than π

Solving problems involving the area of a circle

1 a 225 cm²
  b 78.5 cm²
  c 146.5 cm²
2 a 226.2 cm²   b 113.1 cm²

7.3 Pythagoras' theorem

Calculating the length of the hypotenuse in a right-angled triangle

1 a AB   b FG   c HJ
2 a Sketch of triangle with longest side labelled c
  b 6 cm and 8 cm sides labelled a and b, or vice versa
  c $c = 10$ cm
3 a 13 cm   b 5 cm   c 20 cm
4 26 m

Calculating the length of a shorter side in a right-angled triangle

1 a 9 cm   b 5 cm   c 2 cm
2 a She has not correctly identified the longest side.
  b 40 cm
3 33 cm

7.4 Prisms and cylinders

Calculating the volume of a right prism

1 a 30 cm²
  b 150 cm³
2 a 192 cm³   b 972 cm³
3 Area of cross-section = 44 cm², volume = 440 cm³

Calculating the surface area of a right prism

1 a–b Sketch of net with dimensions labelled
  c 6 cm²
  d 35 cm²
  e 28 cm² and 21 cm²
  f 96 cm²
2 a–b

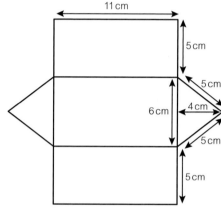

  c Triangular face = 12 cm²
    Rectangular faces = 66 cm² and 55 cm²
  d 200 cm²

Calculating the volume and surface area of a cylinder

1 a 78.5 cm²
  b 785 cm³
2 a 314.2 cm³   b 1206.4 cm³
  c 351.9 cm³
3 a 78.5 cm²
  b 31.4 cm
  c 314 cm²
  d 471 cm²

7.5 Errors and bounds

Finding upper and lower bounds

1 a All of them
  b Any number greater than or equal to 6.5 and less than 7.5, when rounded to the nearest whole number, is 7.
2 a 6.5 cm
  b 7.5 cm
3 a 16

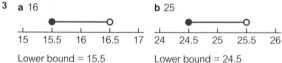

Lower bound = 15.5
Upper bound = 16.5

  b 25

Lower bound = 24.5
Upper bound = 25.5

4 a 17

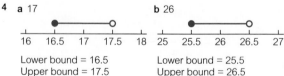

Lower bound = 16.5
Upper bound = 17.5

  b 26

Lower bound = 25.5
Upper bound = 26.5

  c 112

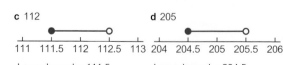

Lower bound = 111.5
Upper bound = 112.5

  d 205

Lower bound = 204.5
Upper bound = 205.5

5 The value on the upper bound does not round to the whole
number given – it would round up to the next whole number.

6 a–b

```
   |          |          |  _____
   |  £4400   |  £4500   | | £4600 |
              |          | |_____|
       £4450      £4550
```

c £4450 ⩽ price of car < £4550

7 £15 ⩽ price of book < £25

Percentage error intervals

1 a, c and **d**

```
   |          |          |  _____
   |  400 g   |  500 g   | | 600 g |
              |          | |_____|
       450 g      550 g
```

b 50 g

e 450 g ⩽ mass of flour < 550 g

2 a 72.1 mph

b 67.9 mph

c 67.9 mph ⩽ speed of car < 72.1 mph

UNIT 8 Graphs

8.1 Using $y = mx + c$

Drawing a graph from its equation

1 a–d

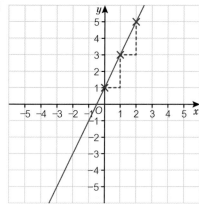

2 a

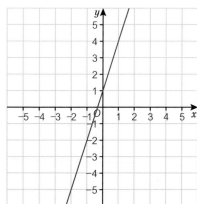

b

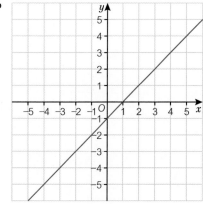

c

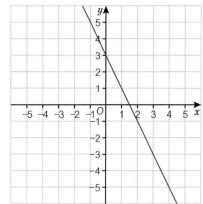

3 b Gradient: 7, y-intercept: $(0, 4)$

c Gradient: -2, y-intercept: $(0, 3)$

d Gradient: 9, y-intercept: $(0, -1)$

4 b Gradient: -3, y-intercept: $(0, 3)$

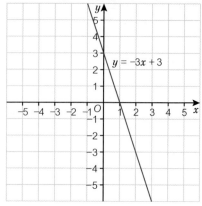

c Gradient: 1, y-intercept: $(0, 4)$

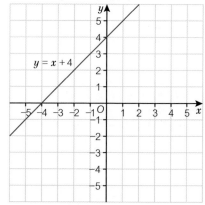

d Gradient: 2, y-intercept: $(0, -1)$

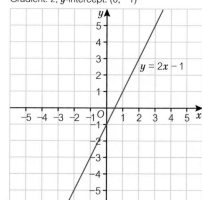

Parallel lines

1 a iv   b ii   c i   d iii

2 b $-3x - 2$ c $2x + 1$

3 b $y = -2x + 1$ c $y = x - 4$

Intersection of lines

1 (2, 7)

2 a (2, 1)   **b** (2, 1)   **c** Same point

3 a (2, 1); not the same coordinates as point (2, 2).

   b and **c i**

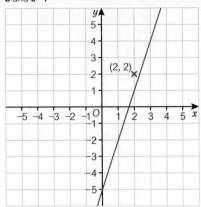

   c ii No   **d** No

8.2 More straight-line graphs

Drawing graphs with equation $ax + by = c$

1 a 2   **b** 4

   c x-intercept   **d** y-intercept

2 a x-intercept: (1, 0), y-intercept: (0, 3)

   b x-intercept: (−1, 0), y-intercept: (0, 2)

   c x-intercept: (7, 0), y-intercept: (0, −7)

   d x-intercept: (2, 0), y-intercept: (0, −5)

3 a x-intercept: (−1, 0), y-intercept: (0, 1)

   b x-intercept: (−2, 0), y-intercept: (0, −1)

   c x-intercept: (1, 0), y-intercept: (0, 1)

4 a

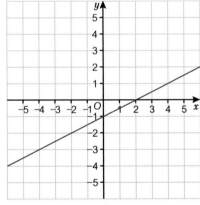

   b

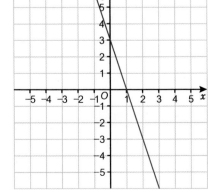

c

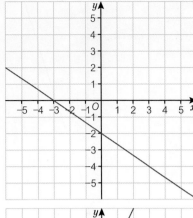

d

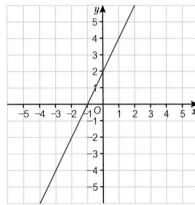

5 a i (2, 0), (0, 2)

     ii (−3, 0), (0, 3)

     iii (2, 0), (0, −6)

     iv (4, 0), (0, −2)

   b i

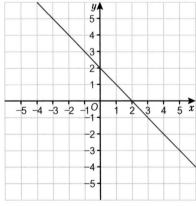

     ii

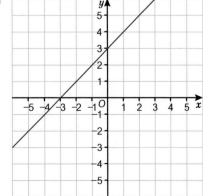

iii

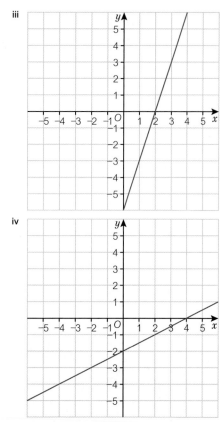

iv

Working with equations of the form $ax + by = c$

1 a i $y = 2x + 7$ ii 2
   b i $y = -3x + 2$ ii −3
   c i $y = 2x + 3$ ii 2
   d i $y = x - 9$ ii 1
2 a Yes   b No   c Yes
3 a $y = 1.5x + 6$ b 1.5
   c $y = 1.5x + 4$
4 a Yes   b No   c Yes
5 a (30, 0), (0, 25)
   b

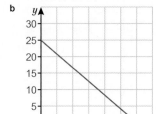

   c Go down
   d i 17   ii 6

8.3 Simultaneous equations

Drawing and solving simultaneous equations

1 a (1, −1)   b (−2, −1)
2 a i 1   ii (0, −3)
   b i −3   ii (0, 1)
   c

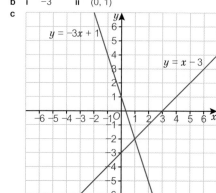

   d (1, −2)
   e $x = 1$ and $y = -2$
   f Students' own check
3 a

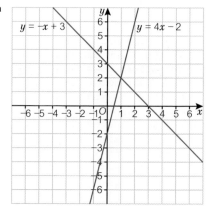

   $x = 1$ and $y = 2$
   b

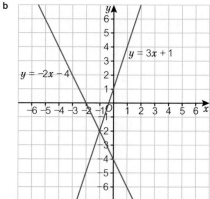

   $x = -1$ and $y = -2$

4 **a** **i** $\frac{1}{2}$ **ii** $(0, -\frac{1}{2})$

    b **i** -3 **ii** $(0, 3)$

    c

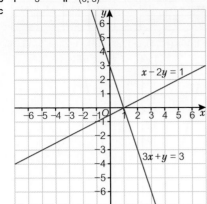

    d $(1, 0)$

    e $x = 1$ and $y = 0$

    f Students' own check

5 **a**

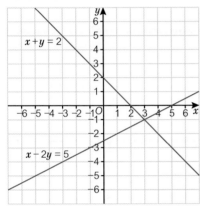

    $x = 3$ and $y = -1$

    b

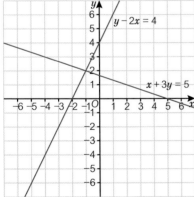

    $x = -1$ and $y = 2$

6

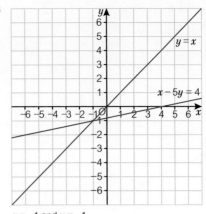

$x = -1$ and $y = -1$

Solving problems with simultaneous equations

1 **a**

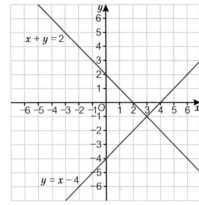

    b $(3, -1)$

2 **a** $x + y = 10$ and $x - y = 2$

    b $(10, 0)$ and $(0, 10)$, $(2, 0)$ and $(0, -2)$

    c

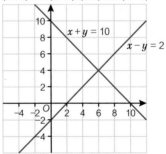

    $x = 6$ and $y = 4$

3 **a** $x + y$ **b** $x + y = 40$

    c $5x + 8y$ **d** $5x + 8y = 290$

    e

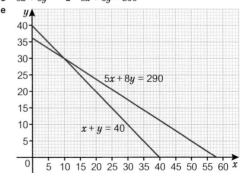

    f $(10, 30)$

    g $x = 10$ and $y = 30$

4 a $x + y = 14$ **b** $7x + 15y = 130$

c

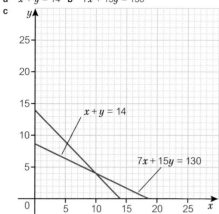

d $x = 10$ and $y = 4$

8.4 Graphs of quadratic functions

Graphs of quadratic equations

1 b 1   **c** 0   **d** 1

2 a

x	−3	−2	−1	0	1	2	3
y	9	4	1	0	1	4	9

b (−3, 9), (−2, 4), (−1, 1), (0, 0), (1, 1), (2, 4), (3, 9)

c and d

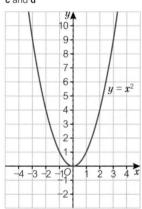

d Yes

3 b 2   **c** 0   **d** 2

4 a

x	−3	−2	−1	0	1	2	3
y	18	8	2	0	2	8	18

b (−3, 18), (−2, 8), (−1, 2), (0, 0), (1, 2), (2, 8), (3, 18)

c and d

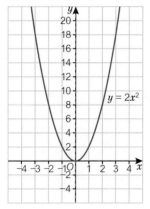

d Yes

5 a False   **b** True   **c** True   **d** True

6 a

x	−3	−2	−1	0	1	2	3
x^2	9	4	1	0	1	4	9
+1	+1	+1	+1	+1	+1	+1	+1
y	10	5	2	1	2	5	10

b (−3, 10), (−2, 5), (−1, 2), (0, 1), (1, 2), (2, 5), (3, 10)

c

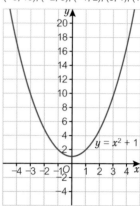

d 17

Problem-solving using graphs of quadratic equations

1 a 36 m   **b** 7.8 m or about 8 m
   c 13 m   **d** 18 m

8.5 More non-linear graphs

Drawing and interpreting non-linear graphs

1 A, C and D

2 a i 8   **ii** 3
   b i 1   **ii** 2

Drawing and interpreting graphs showing inverse proportion

1 a

x	1	2	3	4	6	12
y	12	6	4	3	2	1

b $k = 12$ **c** $y = \dfrac{12}{x}$

d Students' own check   **e** $y = \dfrac{1}{2}$

2 a

Time (hours)	1	2	4
Number of painters	4	2	1

b $k = 4$ **c** 8

3 a 32

b (0, 1), (1, 2), (2, 4), (3, 8), (4, 16), (5, 32)

c

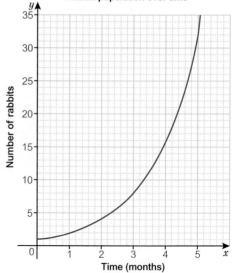

d 3.6 months

4 a £16 000   **b** £12 000   **c** 4 years   **d** 2.4 years

UNIT 9 Probability

9.1 Mutually exclusive events

Mutually exclusive outcomes and events

1 a 4
   b 3
   c $\frac{4}{7}$
   d $\frac{3}{7}$
   e $\frac{2}{7}$
   f $\frac{6}{7}$
   g $\frac{1}{7}$

2 a 5
   b 2, 4, 6
   c 1, 3, 5
   d 3, 6
   e 1, 2, 3, 6
   f 1, 2, 4

3 a No
   b Yes. They have no outcomes in common.

4 B and C

5 a i $\frac{5}{10} = \frac{1}{2}$
      ii $\frac{2}{10} = \frac{1}{5}$
      iii $\frac{3}{10}$
   b i $\frac{7}{10}$
      ii $\frac{8}{10} = \frac{4}{5}$
      iii $\frac{5}{10} = \frac{1}{2}$
   c The outcomes are mutually exclusive because you cannot pick two different colours at once.
   d i   P(R or Y) = $\frac{7}{10}$, P(R) + P(Y) = $\frac{5}{10} + \frac{2}{10} = \frac{7}{10}$
      ii P(R or B) = $\frac{8}{10}$, P(R) + P(B) = $\frac{5}{10} + \frac{3}{10} = \frac{8}{10}$
      iii P(B or Y) = $\frac{5}{10}$, P(B) + P(Y) = $\frac{3}{10} + \frac{2}{10} = \frac{5}{10}$
   e It is the same as the sum of the probabilities of the two separate events.

Probabilities of mutually exclusive outcomes and events

1 a 100%
   b i   0.45
      ii 0.07
      iii 0.48
   c 1

2 35% + 5% + 60% = 100%
   40% + 60% = 100%
   P(G) = 60%

3 a 0.85
   b 0.15

9.2 Experimental and theoretical probability

Probability from experiments

1 a 100
   b 19
   c $\frac{19}{100}$ = 0.19
   d 22
   e $\frac{22}{100} = \frac{11}{50}$ = 0.22
   f 2
   g 4

2 a 40
   b 100
   c 200

3 a 200
   b 400
   c 1000

4 a $\frac{5}{8}$
   b $\frac{3}{8}$
   c More likely to land on red as P(R) = $\frac{5}{8}$ and P(B) = $\frac{3}{8}$.

5 a i   Spinner A has 4 red sections and 2 blue sections.
      ii The probability of landing on red is $\frac{4}{6}$ and on blue is $\frac{2}{6}$.
      iii Landing on red and landing on blue <u>are not</u> equally likely.
   b Yellow
   c Purple

Comparing experimental and theoretical probabilities

1 a i   0.28
      ii 0.21
      iii 0.23
      iv 0.28
   b

Score	Frequency	Experimental probability	Theoretical probability
1	28	0.28	
2	21	0.21	
3	23	0.23	
4	28	0.28	

   c i   0.25
      ii 0.25
      iii 0.25
      iv 0.25
   d

Score	Frequency	Experimental probability	Theoretical probability
1	28	0.28	0.25
2	21	0.21	0.25
3	23	0.23	0.25
4	28	0.28	0.25

2 a

Coin	A	B	C
Number of heads	45	56	23
Experimental probability	0.45	0.56	0.23
Theoretical probability			

   b $\frac{1}{2}$
   c 50
   d Coin A and coin B
   e Coin A and coin B
   f Coin C. The experimental and theoretical probabilities are very different.

3 No correct answer. Most students will probably say B, C, A. Reflect asks them to discuss their answer.

9.3 Sample space diagrams

Drawing sample space diagrams

1 a Heads, tails
   b 1, 2, 3, 4, 5, 6
   c Red, blue, green, yellow

2 a

Spinner A	Spinner B
red	yellow
red	purple
blue	yellow
blue	purple

   b 4
   c 1
   d $\frac{1}{4}$

3 a

Blue dice	Red dice	Outcome
even	even	E, E
even	odd	E, O
odd	even	O, E
odd	odd	O, O

b 2

c $\frac{1}{2}$

4

Blue dice	Even	E, E	O, E
	Odd	E, O	O, O
		Even	Odd
		Red dice	

5 a

Spinner	Coin
1	H
2	H
3	H
1	T
2	T
3	T

b

Coin	Heads	1, H	2, H	3, H
	Tails	1, T	2, T	3, T
		1	2	3
			Spinner	

Probability from a sample space diagram

1 a 4

b 2

c $\frac{2}{4} = \frac{1}{2}$

d 1

e $\frac{1}{4}$

2 a

Red	5	7	8	11
	4	6	7	10
	1	3	4	7
		2	3	6
			Blue	

b 9

c 1

d $\frac{1}{9}$

e 4

f $\frac{4}{9}$

Deciding if a game is fair

1 a

Red	4	5	6	7	8
	3	4	5	6	7
	2	3	4	5	6
	1	2	3	4	5
		1	2	3	4
				Blue	

b i $\frac{8}{16} = \frac{1}{2}$

ii $\frac{8}{16} = \frac{1}{2}$

c Equally likely

d Yes. Both people have the same chance of winning.

e i $\frac{4}{16} = \frac{1}{4}$

ii $\frac{12}{16} = \frac{3}{4}$

f No. Virat is more likely to win.

9.4 Two-way tables

Reading a two-way table

1 a

		Spinner B		
		Blue	Red	Total
Spinner A	Green	30	24	54
	Yellow	22	24	46
	Total	52	48	100

b 54

c 48

d 22

e Green on A, blue on B

Calculating probabilities from a two-way table

1 a 100

b 90

c $\frac{90}{100} = \frac{9}{10} = 0.9$

d 65

e $\frac{65}{100} = \frac{13}{20} = 0.65$

f 4

g $\frac{4}{100} = \frac{1}{25} = 0.04$

h 6

i $\frac{6}{100} = \frac{3}{50} = 0.06$

2 a

		Do you eat breakfast?		
		Yes	No	Total
Year group	Year 7	53	19	72
	Year 8	39	24	63
	Year 9	34	31	65
	Total	126	74	200

b 63

c 24

d $\frac{24}{63}$

e 126

f 53

g $\frac{53}{126}$

3 a

		Spinner B		
		Red	Blue	Total
Spinner A	Red	14	26	40
	Blue	3	7	10
	Total	17	33	50

  b 50
  c 14
  d $\frac{14}{50} = \frac{7}{25}$
  e 29
  f $\frac{29}{50}$
  g $\frac{7}{50}$

4 a

		Book		
		Yes	No	Total
Film	Yes	2	9	11
	No	3	6	9
	Total	5	15	20

  b i $\frac{11}{20}$

   ii $\frac{9}{20}$

  c More likely to have seen a film as the probability is higher.
  d 6
  e 60

9.5 Venn diagrams

Reading a Venn diagram

1 a The prime numbers in the diagram are 2, 3 and 5.
   The multiples of 2 in the diagram are 2, 4 and 6.
  b It is both a prime number and a multiple of 2.
  c 2 is an outcome of both events.
  d 1 is not a prime number or a multiple of 2; it is not an
   outcome of either event.

Probability from a Venn diagram

1 a 6
  b 3
  c $\frac{3}{6} = \frac{1}{2}$
  d $\frac{4}{6} = \frac{2}{3}$
  e 2
  f $\frac{2}{6} = \frac{1}{3}$

Drawing Venn diagrams and calculating probabilities

1 a

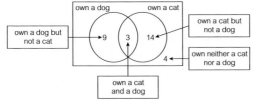

  b i There are 9 + 3 + 14 + 4 = 30 students in
   the Venn diagram.
   ii 14 students own a cat but not a dog.
   iii 17 students own a cat.
   iv 3 students own a cat and a dog.
   v 4 students own neither a cat nor a dog.

  c i $\frac{14}{30} = \frac{7}{15}$

   ii $\frac{17}{30}$

   iii $\frac{3}{30} = \frac{1}{10}$

   iv $\frac{4}{30} = \frac{2}{15}$

2 a 7
  b 6
  c 7
  d

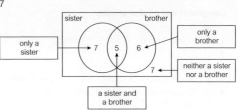

  e i $\frac{7}{25}$

   ii $\frac{5}{25} = \frac{1}{5}$

   iii $\frac{13}{25}$

UNIT 10 Comparing shapes

10.1 Congruent and similar shapes

Congruent and similar shapes

1 a C   b B
2 a A and C   b A and B, B and C
3 d i *DF*   ii *EF*
   e 3, 3, 3
   f Yes, the ratios of the corresponding sides are all the same.
4 a Similar, scale factor of enlargement 2
   b Neither
   c Similar, scale factor of enlargement $\frac{1}{5}$
   d Similar, scale factor of enlargement 4

Using congruent shapes to solve problems

1

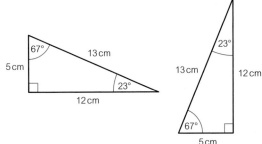

2 a A and C
   b A and B
   c A and C
   d A and C
3 The sides of length 10 cm are **not** corresponding sides: on the first triangle it is the longest side; on the second it isn't. Even if the unknown angles in each triangle were the same, the triangles wouldn't be congruent.
4 a–b Students' diagrams
   c Yes
   d Yes, since there is only one length, they will always be enlargements of one another.

10.2 Ratios in triangles

Sides in similar triangles

1 a Side *AC* corresponds to side *DF*.
     Side *BC* corresponds to side *EF*.
   b i 1 : 3   ii 1 : 3   iii 1 : 3
   c All the ratios are the same.
   d If two triangles are similar the ratios of the lengths of corresponding sides are equal.
2 a 12 : 6   b 2 : 1
   c 10 : 5, *AC* = 10 cm   d 8 : 4, *EF* = 4 cm
3 a i 7 : 9
     ii 4 : 6
     iii 10 : 12
   b 7 : 9, 2 : 3 and 5 : 6
   c No
   d If triangles are similar all the ratios are the same.

Angles in similar triangles

1 a 37°, 53°, 90°
   b Corresponding angles are equal.
   c 39°, 49°, 92°
   d Corresponding angles are equal.
   e In similar triangles corresponding angles are <u>equal</u>.
2 a Corresponding angles are not equal.
   b Corresponding sides are not in the same ratio to each other.
   c Corresponding angles are not equal.

10.3 The tangent ratio

Naming the sides of a right-angled triangle

1 a *BC*   b *DE*   c *GI*
2 a *AB*   b *EF*   c *GH*

Using the tangent ratio

1 a–c 1
   d i 0.3   ii 0.6   iii 1.7   iv 0

2 a–c $\tan 20° = \frac{y}{8}$
   d $y = 8 \times \tan 20°$
   e $y = 2.9$ cm
3 a 3.5 cm   b 12 cm   c 7.0 cm
4 a 10.4 cm   b 12 cm   c 32.2 cm
5 A: $\tan 30° = \frac{3}{x}$

   B: $\tan 30° = \frac{x}{3}$

10.4 The sine ratio

Finding the hypotenuse of a right-angled triangle

1 a *AC*   b *DF*   c *GI*
2 a The hypotenuse is the longest side. It is opposite the right angle.
   b The opposite side to angle θ is opposite the angle θ.
   c The adjacent side to angle θ is next to θ and the right angle.

Using the sine ratio

1 a–c 0.5 or $\frac{1}{2}$
   d i 0.3   ii 0.7   iii 0.9
   iv 1   v 0

2 a–c $\sin 30° = \frac{y}{9}$
   d $y = 9 \times \sin 30°$
   e $y = 4.5$ cm
3 a 7.1 cm   b 10.4 cm   c 2.9 cm
4 a 13.4 cm   b 5.5 cm   c 8.8 cm
5 A: $\sin 62° = \frac{y}{10}$

   B: $\tan 62° = \frac{y}{11}$

10.5 The cosine ratio

Using the cosine ratio

1 a–c 0.5 or $\frac{1}{2}$
   d i 1.0   ii 0.9   iii 0.7
     iv 0   v 1

2 a–c $\cos 30° = \frac{y}{10}$
   d $y = 10 \times \cos 30°$
   e $y = 8.7$ cm
3 a 8.5 cm   b 7.5 cm   c 9.2 cm
4 a 11.5 cm   b 6.1 cm   c 31.4 cm
5 A: $\sin 50° = \frac{12}{y}$

   B: $\cos 50° = \frac{18}{y}$

6 He has incorrectly identified the sides; y = opposite.

10.6 Using trigonometry to find angles

The inverse tangent function

1 a–c 45°
   d i 63.4°   ii 71.6°   iii 26.6°
     iv 74.1°   v 79.1°
2 a–c $\tan \theta = \frac{4}{3}$ d 53.1°
3 a 40.6°   b 59.0°   c 63.4°

The inverse sine function

1 a–c 30°
   d i 53.1°   ii 11.5°   iii 14.5°
     iv 81.9°   v 44.4°
2 a–c $\sin \theta = \frac{12}{13}$ d 67.4°
3 a 38.7°   b 30°   c 22.0°

The inverse cosine function

1 a–c 60°
   d i 36.9°   ii 78.5°   iii 75.5°
     iv 8.1°   v 45.6°
2 a–c $\cos \theta = \frac{9}{14}$ d 650.0°
3 a 64.6°   b 68.7°   c 48.2°

Index